The Sh... Fl... nds

A NATURAL H...LOWS

For
Mavis and Jack;
Anne, Francis and Ruth.

Stephen Heery

The Shannon Floodlands
A NATURAL HISTORY OF THE SHANNON CALLOWS

TírEolas

Published by Tír Eolas 1993
Newtownlynch, Kinvara, Co. Galway

© Stephen Heery
ISBN 1 873821 026

Layout and design: Anne Korff
Typesetting: Johan Hofsteenge
Printed by Colour Books

Contents

Acknowledgements

I would like to thank all the people who helped and encouraged me in this book, and all those whom I have met on the Callows in the past decade. In particular, I thank the following who kindly read through, and commented on, early drafts of different chapters: James Scully, Charles Meredith, Christy Cunniffe, John Feehan, Ian Herbert, Oscar Merne, Richard Nairn and Jim Ryan. Any errors and omissions are, of course, entirely my own.

For financial assistance I would like to thank: Shannon Development Co. (in particular, Joe Price and Éamonn De Stafort); Bord na Mona (in particular Tom Lucas of Blackwater Works); and Office of Public Works (in particular Noel Treacy T.D. and Minister of State).

I am very grateful to the three local artists who have accurately portrayed the Callows flowers, birds and landscape: to Anne O'Connell, who drew the flowers from Callows specimens and produced the pencil drawings of assorted Callows features; to Gordon D'Arcy who brought his knowledge of wetlands and his artistic skill together to produce ink drawings of Callows birds; and to Lorraine Francis for capturing the general Callows landscape with ink studies. The Corncrake on the Irish Wildbird Conservancy leaflet, reproduced in Chapter 5, was drawn by Don Conroy.

For photographic material: Ian Herbert (courtesy of National Trust of Northern Ireland) for the Water Rail; Richard Nairn for the aerial view on the front cover; Oscar Merne for the aerial view of the Little Brosna; Richard T. Mills for the calling Corncrake, Heron and Pintail; Mrs Liston, of Banagher, who allowed her eighty-year old Glossy Ibis to be photographed; and Margaret Barton, of Lusmagh, for the photograph of a Callows hay meadow in the 1960s.

I also thank all those who have allowed unpublished work to be used: in particular, Aloys Hooyer for work on the soft geology beneath the Little Brosna callows; Eoin Shaw for material from his Young Scientist Exhibition project; and the Irish Wildbird Conservancy for material on their Corncrake and breeding bird studies.

Preface

For many generations the floodplain, or callows, of the central Shannon basin have been seen as an area crying out for arterial drainage and reclamation, in the interests of agricultural improvement and the prevention of flooding of lands, homesteads and roads. Undoubtedly such drainage and reclamation would be technically feasible nowadays, but the economic costs would be enormous. In recent times, too, many have come to realise that the callows are not just areas which could be turned into intensive farmland, but are a unique feature of the Irish landscape and a vital part of our natural heritage. While such floodplains have steadily disappeared throughout western Europe the callows remain as a wonderful example of the richness and diversity of this kind of habitat. There are few places in the world where one can find the herb-rich grasslands and wetlands of the callows, with their vast numbers of waterfowl during the winter months, and the summer full of the "drumming" of Snipe. The Shannon Callows are now the main stronghold of the Corncrake which was once a common summer visitor.

The callows are not entirely natural and their value to the abundant flora and fauna depends heavily on the traditional type of agriculture which has been practiced there. As the Common Agricultural Policy undergoes radical changes, from a heavy emphasis on intensive production to one with greater concern for the environment, it is possible that farmers may fear a serious reduction in their living standards. But while grant aid in the past has been given for intensification, grants in the future will be given for environmentally friendly farming practices, particularly in areas of high ecological value. The callows are such an area, as will be evident from this excellent book, and it is to be hoped that means will be found to maintain the harmonious relationship between the needs of the farming community which manages the lands, and the needs of the wildlife for which the area is internationally famous. The river, its callows, the flora and fauna, and the traditional way of farming the wetlands are a major part of our national heritage, and as such deserve our best efforts to ensure their continuance.

As Minister with responsibility for the conservation of wildlife I welcome the publication of this fine book, which will help to engender a greater understanding and wider appreciation of the Shannon Callows as an outstanding example of a disappearing wetland habitat.

I would also like to acknowledge the interest of my predecessor, Mr. Noel Treacy, T.D., in promoting this publication.

Noel Dempsey

Noel Dempsey, T.D.,
Government Chief Whip and Minister of State at the Department of Finance.

April, 1993.

Foreword

This Ireland of ours has been inhabited by Man for 9,000 years at least, and the slow and cumulative cultural inheritance of all those millenia has endowed the landscape with a uniquely rich heritage. On the other hand, the long-continued pressure on the land by human communities within our circumscribed island living space has gradually pushed back the frontiers of the natural world, so that we now have few areas where much of its original diversity still survives. Those areas where the natural endowment has accommodated itself to agricultural practice are among the richest and most precious of Irish landscapes, and one of these areas, the flooded grasslands along the Shannon, is the subject of this wonderful book. The callows have evolved with the human cultures surrounding them, providing grass in spring from the earliest days of Irish agriculture and hay in autumn in more recent centuries. An echo of this early use of the callows for spring grazing still survives in placenames within a stone's throw of the river: places like Boolanarrig, the spring grazing, Annaghanerrig, the spring marshes.

This is a critical time for the future of the Midlands landscape, as we begin for the first time to give serious thought to what needs to be done now if the landscape of the future is to maintain the maximum of ecological diversity: and if we are to ensure that ecological values are fully integrated in management plans, as a new landscape evolves following the retreat of the last wilderness of the bogs. Not primarily because a landscape with the maximum of richness and diversity is important to those with special interests in such things as birds or flowers, archaeology or sedimentology, but because it is the heritage of the whole community. Books like Stephen Heery's enable the community and its visitors to make that heritage fully their own, so that they may plan for the future with a deeper understanding of its value. The book is a model of its kind, and it should be in every household in the Midlands, in the hand of every traveller.
It is no accident that many of the hermits of the 8th and 9th century Irish church looked to the wooded wilderness of the Shannon floodplain for their retreats. What they sought was the world as God made it, and they found in that rich landscape the inspiration for Europe's first real nature poetry. One of those early poets, writing in the 9th century at Lemonaghan, on the edge of the callows, with the voice of the 7th century founder of Lemonaghan, Manchan of Liath, celebrated the landscape of remote forest and stream of the medieval landscape of the south Midlands in verses which are among the finest in early Irish nature poetry.

The inspiration, the joy that inspired those early nature poets, is still to be found on the callows. It is up to us to make sure that some poet of 1000 years hence can still find here the inspiration that broke into such song in the words of the hermit who spoke in Manchan's voice. Stephen Heery is its new chronicler - in the tradition of the great Tigemach who penned his Annals within sight and sound of the same river that Stephen celebrates. His work will go a long way to ensure that the river and its callows will always inspire.

John Feehan
Birr, Easter 1993

Prologue

The River Shannon inscribes a long-tailed 'S' on the centre of Ireland as it flows between Lough Ree and Lough Derg. Every winter the river channel fills and floods the surrounding fields. These fields are the Shannon Callows - thirty-five square kilometres from which hay is made and on which cattle graze in summer when the floods have retreated. Floods in an agricultural landscape have always favoured wildlife, and wild nature exists here in year-round abundance and variety which is among the best in north-west Europe.

The Shannon Callows are considered to be outstanding and of international importance in the total numbers and variety of wildfowl and wading birds which return to feed there each winter. Four of these are listed by the E.C. as requiring special conservation measures to protect the places where they congregate. In summer, wading birds nest in numbers equalled only by two places in Ireland and Britain. Two rare breeding birds in Ireland, and the globally-endangered Corncrake find nest sites, and seventeen plant species, loosely classed as 'rare', survive on the Callows. But this is only half the story.

This book is about a place - the Shannon Callows. It is mainly about the plant-life, bird-life, the landscape and the farming. It is intended that the book provide a picture of the Callows as they are known at present, glimpses of the Callows of the past, and a look to the future of the Callows as a very special place and an irreplaceable part of Ireland's (and Europe's) heritage.

Chapter one introduces the Callows and its place in the landscape of central Ireland. Chapter two describes the genesis of the Callows since the Ice Age and takes the reader back to the great lake that covered the area. Chapter three deals with the one feature that gives the Callows their character, annual flooding. Chapter 4 puts most of the very varied forms of flowers, grasses, rushes and sedges in an ecological context and lists the two hundred or so plant species which survive on the Callows today. Chapter 5 describes the succession of abundant and varied bird-life - the most conspicuous part of nature on the Callows. Chapter 6 describes farming on these temperamental grasslands. Finally, Chapter 7 follows the chronology of research and observation of nature on the Callows and looks at the Callows as a place where nature, farming and tourism can co-exist far beyond the twenty-first century.

"that precious stretch of meadowland"

Introducing the Shannon, the Callows and the book

The River Shannon

The River Shannon has been the subject of writing for a long time past but especially since the middle of the eighteenth century. Over these centuries the River has been written about from many different points of view, in many styles and through changing social conditions of the people who lived on its banks. In the eighteenth century (indeed as early as the sixteenth) the River seemed to be ideal for inland navigation from the sea, which would provide over two hundred extra miles of 'coastline'. The first report was commissioned in 1715. By 1755 travellers could sail from Killaloe to Carrick with the help of canals by-passing the few 'rapid' sections of the River at Meelick, Banagher, Shannonbridge and Athlone. This was the start of more than two centuries of pen on paper about the River - extolling its beauty, lamenting its wilderness, regarding it as an opportunity to develop the country, or viewing it as an engineering problem.

The importance of the River for travel through the midlands of Ireland in the nineteenth century cannot be over-emphasised. One commentator, who was widely travelled in Ireland and Europe, thought the road from Banagher to Athlone in 1834 the worst he had seen in Ireland. Only an inconvenient timetable prevented him from travelling by steam riverboat to Athlone at 2d per mile (1).

Even today much of what has been written has come from those who have had a long affair with the Shannon via the Inland Waterways Association of Ireland. In *'By Shannon's Shores'* (2), and others, we read of legends which merge into fact about early Irish tribes along the River; traders from France before the time of Christ; sixth century monastic settlements springing up and passing through centuries of fame and destruction; great early nineteenth century fortifications of neatly dressed stone, still standing because they were never seriously threatened; nineteenth and twentieth century struggles, verbal and practical, in copious reports and by labourers in the River channel itself, to stem the floods and improve navigation.

R.L.Praeger thought the Shannon "a curious river" (3) on account of its strange course from a short torrential stream in the Cuilcagh Mountains in Co. Cavan, through low-lying lakes and floodplains along most of its course, to its confinement among the Arra and Slieve Bernagh mountains at the end - almost the opposite of a more conventional river. The bedrock under the Shannon is Carboniferous Limestone for most of its course but the coal formations which nineteenth century geologists thought held promise for Ireland turned out not to be the great Coal Measures such as fuelled the Industrial Revolution in Britain.

THE LORDLY SHANNON

"The River Shannon, that great river which penetrates the interior of Ireland, navigable from ocean to source, rising in one coalfield, emptying itself into another, and washing the banks of our most fertile counties, delivers into the sea . . . water from 3613 square miles" 1846 (15)

"On the whole face of the globe probably no river exists in so large a size in proportion to that of the island through which it flows" 1832 (8)

The facts about the River are these. It is a short distance from where the River rises, at the Shannon Pot in the hills of Co. Cavan, to Lough Allen. In its long 205km journey from Lough Allen to Lough Derg the River drops only 12m, which means it has the shallowest gradient of any large river in Europe. Below Lough Derg, Parteen Weir and a diversion allow the entire fall of the River below Meelick, and a volume of almost six cubic kilometres of water every year, to be harnessed by the Ardnacrusha Hydro-electric Power Station. The power thus generated is equivalent to 'free' fuel for the cities of Limerick, Cork and Galway combined. It is a short distance from here to the sea at Limerick.

The Shannon receives water from twelve counties of Ireland, and from many lakes: from Lough Sheelin, Lough Owel, and Lough Derravaragh via the River Inny; from Lough Ennell via the River Brosna; from Lough Gara and Lough Key via the River Boyle; and from the more obscure Lough O'Flynn, in County Roscommon, via the River Suck. Rains and alluvium make their way to the Shannon from the Old Red Sandstone and Silurian hills of Slieve Bloom via the Little Brosna River and its tributary, the Camcor River, and via tributaries of the River Brosna itself - the Silver and Clodiagh Rivers.

A recent commentator (1990) saw the Shannon and its catchment as a great "gutter-like depression" in the Centre of Ireland from which water escapes to the sea only with difficulty (4). This is a most apt analogy which is explored further in Chapter 3. Nowhere is this phenomenon more pronounced than on the Shannon and the Little Brosna Callows which lie alongside the Middle Shannon from the town of Athlone to Portumna, between Lough Ree and Lough Derg, two of Ireland's largest lakes (Map 1).

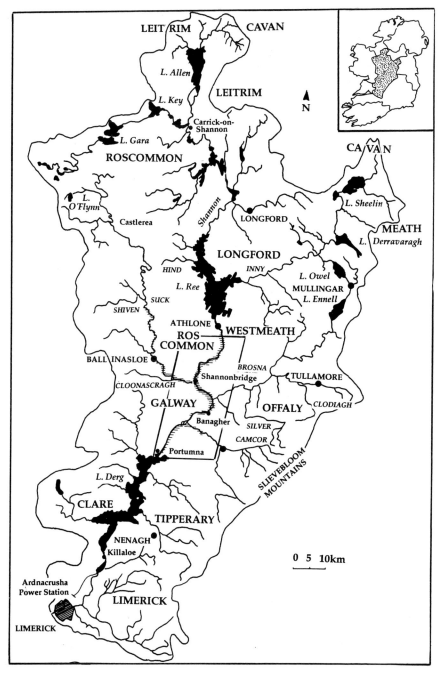

MAP 1: The catchment of the River Shannon

The River Shannon receives water from twelve counties, and inscribes a long-tailed 'S' on the Centre of Ireland as it flows between Lough Ree and Lough Derg.

The Middle Shannon, the Callows

The Irish word 'caladh' means a river meadow implying, from times long before arterial drainage tamed any rivers, fields which flood during the winter months but which dry out enough in summer for use as hay and pasture. The anglicised word 'callow' was used in the early part of the nineteenth century for lands liable to flood beside the River Shannon. It has probably always been in local usage although 'bottom meadows', 'water meadows', 'flood meadows', 'wet meadows', 'river flats', 'damaged or affected lands', 'lands liable to floods', and 'lowland wet grassland' have all been used as synonyms in various reports and accounts through the years. The word 'callow' did not appear at all in a major report of the Flood Problem in 1956. It has again come into general usage since attention to the wildfowl in the late sixties led to a more intimate local knowledge of these 'floodplain grasslands'.

Few callows survived the arterial drainage campaign of the late 1950s to late 1970s in other catchments. Six callows, spread widely in Counties Mayo, Kildare, Galway, Clare and Wexford, were former feeding sites of geese, now abandoned due to arterial drainage (5). Perhaps the 250 hectares Lismore Callows on the River Blackwater in Co. Waterford are the best remaining away from the Shannon. It is significant that virtually the last remaining callowland in Ireland, the Shannon Callows, is also the most extensive, and indeed was probably always the most extensive, even in the days before the taming of floods. They survive only because the flood problem has appeared intractable.

'Caladh' can also mean 'landing place', for instance in the recent Irish translation of Shannon Harbour, where the Grand Canal meets the River, as 'Caladh na Sionainne' on a signpost near Banagher (Illus. 1.1). Other names (from a geography textbook of the 1950s) for Shannon Harbour are Cluain Uaine Beag and Caladhphuirt na Sionainne.

Illus. 1.1 Caladh na Sionainne (near Banagher, Co. Offaly)

'caladh' here means landing place or harbour, not the flood meadows.
(Photo: S. Heery)

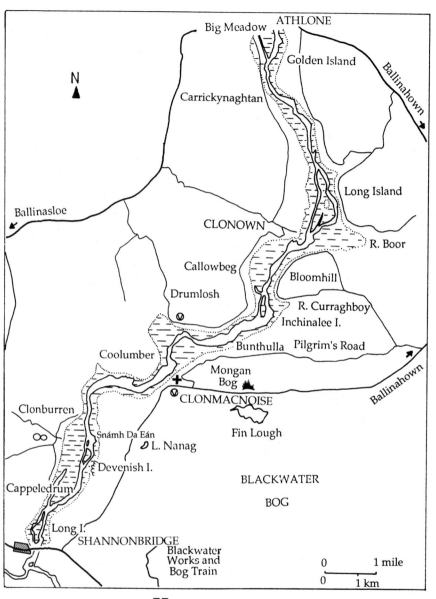

MAP 2 a, b, c: The Shannon Callows, showing place-names mentioned in the text. and landmarks around the Callows.

≡ The Callows, alongside the River Shannon.

✚ Old church, Meelick, Clonfert and Clonmaicnoise.

∞ Norman Motte and Bailey, Clonburren.

■ Castles.

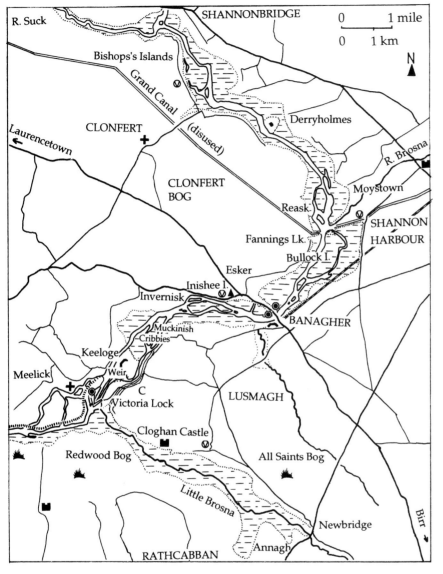

Three thousand five hundred continuous hectares of callowland exist alongside the Middle Shannon (including the Little Brosna) and the figure rises to five thousand to include callowland beside the River Suck.

If the gradient of the whole River is slight, then that of the Middle Shannon is spectacularly so. During flood only five metres separates the height of Lough Ree and Lough Derg, and almost four of these are taken up by locks at Lusmagh and Athlone. This means that the River between the Callows, which is, after all, half the total channel length of the whole River, has an infinitesimal gradient. The River falls just thirty-five centimetres between Athlone and Shannonbridge (6).

The traveller southwards along the Shannon enters a very different riverscape on leaving the town of Athlone than the one left behind on entering Lough Ree, and the Callows are an integral part of that landscape. To many, comparing the landscape with more conventional scenic beauty, it has seemed monotonous, especially from the low vantage point of the River itself.

"To the lover of the picturesque, the banks of the Shannon between Portumna and Banagher present little that is attractive." 1834 (1)

"The landscape, in any artistic sense of the word, is totally wanting, the country all around being nearly

⊙   Martello Tower, Banagher and 'Meelick' tower (Napoleonic), early nineteenth century.

ↄ   'Battery' (Napoleonic fort), Banagher (Fort Eliza) and Keeloge. Early nineteenth century.

▨   Napoleonic 'bridgehead' fortification and barracks (Shannonbridge), early nineteenth century.

C   Clonahenoge canal (disused).

⋘   Victoria Lock, Lusmagh and 'New Cut'.

▲   Old schoolhouse, Esker.

⫽   Old track of Clara-Banagher Railway Co.

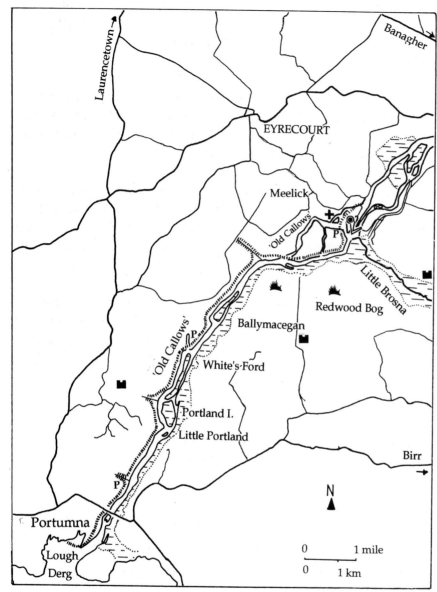

Shannon Scheme Embankment, built 1929.

P Pumphouse on Shannon Scheme Embankment (1929).

Wet, intact bog of conservation interest.

Rocks of Clorhane (opposite Devenish Island).

Good views of the Callows from public roads.

(inclusion of a landmark on this map does not imply right of access to private property)

dead level, much of it morass and a considerable portion under periodic inundation...low, flat, boggy and irksome." 1896 (7)

Fields that in any case are wide and flat, with few trees and often devoid of fences, can be obscured by tall reeds and a rise towards the river bank. In the past, and I suspect today, the scenic highlights from the River were the signs of habitation - the low hills and round towers of Clonmacnoise, the angular fortifications of Shannonbridge, and the two spires of Banagher. But if the viewpoint is reversed and the Callows are seen from these elevated vantage points their true place in the landscape is better appreciated. The juxtaposition of green Callows and brown bogs has been perceived in two ways. In the nineteenth century "the strong contrast of extreme fertility and barrenness" was commented upon. At least in those days the bogs had a clothing of heather which, in August, must have surpassed the Callows in colour. The vast, brown, machine-harvested bogs of today contrast even more. But for one commentator the Callows were dwarfed by the surrounding bogs and considered to be "merely reclaimed portions of the Bog of Allen." (8)

All writers seem to agree that the stretch from Banagher to Meelick is different and beyond criticism. The sight of gentleman's seats (such as Shannongrove and Invernisk) set in parkland close to the River must have been reassuring. To many travellers (for instance, H.D.Inglis in 1834) the wooded areas on the islands were a welcome relief from the "wide and apparently interminable" callows south of Meelick and the bogs north of Banagher which were to him "even more uninteresting than the meadows between Portumna and Banagher".

In 1852 the Abbey of Meelick, although dilapidated, was situated on "a beautiful wooded eminence" (9). The church at Meelick has recently been finely restored but the woods have gone, replaced by beautifully and locally crafted interior woodwork.

Of course, impressions of the Callows are influenced by the seasonal and weather contrasts and the writer's particular viewpont. Today, a mere casual inspection looking for teeming wildbirds can meet with either disappointment or elation depending on the time of year or even the time of day. A wide and exposed landscape that looks wonderful under blue skies can become decidedly unattractive in cold rain. Charles Lever (from Moate, Co. Westmeath) was a writer of novels set in the real Midlands landscape of his time. In 1842 he had a character alighting from the flyboat along the Grand Canal, looking over the Callows at Shannon Harbour and thinking "a prospect more bleak, more desolate and more barren it would be impossible to conceive" (10), while four years earlier a different (real) travel writer said of the same place "It is still indeed a swamp but very beautiful" (11).

The Callows defined

The Callows are the fields that flood in winter and spring beside the River Shannon. But in summer, when the grass is green, cattle graze and the hay is tall, it is possible for a visitor to look at the scene and ask "Where are the Callows ?" They have heard of the floods and that flocks of wildfowl come, but that is no help when looking at the pastoral scene before them. In fact, local features distinguish the very distinct Callows landscape from the 'upland'.

THREE OPINIONS

"We now advance on a portion of the River of singular beauty. Numerous islands, clothed in wood of most graceful character; banks, the greenest on the Shannon and dotted with cattle whose sleek sides and comfortable proportions tell of the richness of their pasture... a picture not easily forgotten." 1852 (9)

"A prospect more bleak, more desolate and more barren it would be impossible to conceive - a wide river with low and reedy banks moving sluggishly on its yellow current between broad tracts of bog or callow meadowland, no trace of cultivation, not even a tree was seen." 1842 (10)

"I do not know that, in viewing natural scenery I have ever felt emotions more new and more delightful. Romantic associations that are suspended while the world is present came back upon my heart and I felt that I was enjoying the reality of a dream." 1838 (11)

No houses new, old or derelict occupy the Callows and almost no tarred roads traverse them. Hedges of hawthorn ('ditches' in the Irish sense), planted to enclose fields on better-drained land in the l9th century, find no place on the Callows. Instead, individual willows and alders stand out along the drains, making the Callows seem almost treeless. The Callows fields look large because boundaries often are fenceless field drains - 'wet fences' - and ownership is shared by a number of farmers. In particular, hay meadow fields are large, hiding the fact that very many farmers own sometimes narrow strips, delineated by nothing except marker stones hidden among the grass at their extremities. Or, if these stones have disappeared under grass and soil like young archaeological relics, fertiliser bags hung on bushes do the same job.

The Callows fields are flat, a level surface built up by level floods. Relief of more than one metre is virtually absent. The Callows as a whole are a sinuous, relatively narrow wetland: in a few places they are only as wide as the River; often the distance from Callows edge to Callows edge is half a mile; and in a few notable places - Shannon Harbour, Clonburren, Clonmacnoise and Clonown - the Callows are a mile wide.

More objectively, the boundaries of the Callows can be set with reference to the plant communities described in Chapter 4.

Crossing the Callows

In history, the Callows have made a large River even more difficult to bridge or ford. When the first bridges were being built the Callows were at least partly flooded for half the year, and generations of bridges have existed at each site since. Bridges have always held a fascination, perhaps because the bridging of a river is the occasion of Man's most frequent and essential struggles with natural forces. Elevation profiles of all the bridges over the Shannon were drawn by Thomas Rhodes for the Commissioners in 1833 and are reproduced in *The Shell Guide to the Shannon*. This includes a wooden structure at Shannon Harbour built to carry horses towing the Grand canal flyboats crossing the River to continue the canal journey. A stone bridge was present at Banagher around 1049 AD, and another was built to span the River at Shannonbridge in 1759. Visitors to Clonmacnoise 'before 1200 AD' could cross the River on a wooden bridge. This was destroyed by the English in 1552 (12). Floods destroyed a long, and perhaps precarious, wooden bridge at Portumna in 1814. Even in the driest of seasons the Callows remained soft and damp, and have controlled the positions of the major bridging points since. Today the only road bridges, at Athlone, at Shannonbridge twenty four kilometres downstream, and at Banagher a further thirteen kilometres away, are built where the Callows are non-existent. At these places the River crosses eskers, the flood is restricted and dry firm ground occurs on both sides of the River (Map 3). There are exceptions to this pattern. There is no bridge at Keeloge where solid rock enfolds the River, and in the 1980s two 'rail' bridges were built by Bord na Mona spanning the Shannon and the Suck where harvested bogs come down to the River.

Illus. 1.2 High flood at Shannon Harbour by Lorraine Francis 1991

A section of the Clara-Banagher railway line, abandoned and dismantled in 1963, skirts the Callows near Shannon Harbour. "since the floodwater occasionally covered the trackway, the train often entered the town like a great snorting amphibious reptile". The track is seen here during floods which eventually entered houses at Shannon Harbour in February 1990.

Illus. 1.3 Lamb or Long Island and the Clonburren callows from Shannonbridge by Lorraine Francis 1992

Two Africans recently thought the view from Shannonbridge lacked only giraffe to remind them of home. The stonewall in this picture is part of the grand, unique and perfectly preserved angular fortifications built by the British in the early nineteenth century to repel possible French invaders at the crossing point.

Fords existed before these bridges and at other (bridgeless) sites such as Keeloge, near Meelick. Meelick almost had a bridge. The Clara & Banagher Railway Co. opened a branch line to Banagher in 1884 with the abandoned intention of crossing the River at Meelick. The line skirts the Callows on its two mile approach to Banagher (Illus. 1.2) and "since the Shannon floodwater occasionally covered the trackway, the train often entered the town like a great snorting amphibious reptile." (13). It was abandoned to nature in 1963, and like all such railway lines, has become a place of great conservation interest, an invaluable complement to the callows it borders.

As thousands of years of river sand and gravel were removed during excavation to improve navigation at Keeloge in 1844, artifacts were recovered which showed that men and women had been crossing the River at this point back into misty Neolithic time. In 1990, an archaeological search of the river bed at Coreen Ford on the River Suck, in preparation for the long-awaited navigational improvements (it was first surveyed in 1802), turned up an astonishing variety of artifacts. From the Stone Age to Modern Times there was a classic esker crossing place here, which had played a part in every major event in the area's history. Beside the ford was a Medieval Fort and possibly an earlier crannog (a small stockaded settlement surrounded by marsh and floodwater) on the same site. Among the everyday belongings found here were: a late-Bronze Age sword and pottery; late-Christian era ploughshare; a Viking battle-axe; Medieval thimbles, buckles and stirrups; and eighteenth century musket balls and military buttons (Archaeological Survey of Co. Galway, University College, Galway). Crossing places have also existed where dry ground lay opposite Callows, possibly involving landing places.

From ancient times the gateway to and from the West lay across the Clonburren callows where the Pilgrim's Road (which ran east-west across Ireland along eskers via Clonmacnoise) crossed the Shannon at a small island called Snámh Dá Éan (Swim two Birds) (14). For ages, when the bogs of today were still low marshy places, this was apparently the only crossing of the Shannon between Athlone and Lough Derg. The remains of a small castle, built by the O'Kellys on the riverbank at the ford around 850 AD, can still be seen surrounded by water at high flood. The Normans built the impressive, and still preserved, Motte and Bailey castle overlooking the Clonburren callows in 1180 and O'Kelly's castle was still manned as a garrison in 1691. The Corncrake, Redshank and Shoveler that inhabit Snámh Dá Éan today provide a living link with a long chain of human history on the callows of Clonburren.

Further north, around 950 AD, another route, a cobbled road - O'Roarke's road - led from the north-west over the bog at Coolumper down to a wooden bridge over the River to Clonmacnoise.

The Callows were an obstacle to major transport of the outside world passing over and beyond the River. But the yearly rise and fall of the River over the Callows permeated the lives of those living on its banks, not always in a restrictive way. It has been suggested that the common prefix to Callows place names - "Cluain" - means 'a fertile area cut off by bog or river', or simply 'meadow'. In some settlements along the River, for instance Clonown and Clonfert, facing the Callows and with their backs to the great bogs, crossing the Shannon was easier than going over the bogs to meet the main upland roads. The local history of Clonown parish shows this well (12). In the early 20th century the people of Curraghboy on the Leinster side would cross the River to go to Mass in Clonown on the Connaught side every Sunday morning "winter and summer, flood or low" in their flat-bottomed cots. In the 1920s a dancehall in Clonown became "the mecca of dancers on either side of the Shannon". Children from Lusmagh crossed the River for schooling at Meelick.

Consequently, many 'trans-Shannon' marriages took place - eighteen such marriages have been documented in Clonown for the period 1870 to 1900 (12). If the genealogy of the older generation were studied, people who grew up on the edges of the Callows would be found to have more in common with those on the opposite bank than with those of the 'upland'. The people of Clonfert Callows rented and farmed their 'bog gardens'; cut, sold and loaded turf on to the boats of people from big houses as far away as Co. Tipperary; cut hay for the landowners of Bishop's Islands; and beat grouse on the Bog for the gentry. Haycocks were taken out of the fertile Bishop's Islands Callows by boat. The last inhabitants of a cluster of cottages at Reask, sheltered from the wind, but not from the floods, by alders and Scot's pines, lived there in the 1940s. A low-lying, vehicleless, cobbled track leads there between the Bog and the Callows from Fanning's Lock at the end of the dry and defunct western extension of the Grand Canal.

A collection of callows

Today, access is much easier for both the farmer and the naturalist. But even so no road runs parallel to the River for long, and the Callows may mistakenly seem like a series of disconnected wetlands. Nothing is further from the truth. Each individual section, with its own name in the singular - Inch callow, Bridge callow, Foolagh callow, Tower callow, Park callow and many more - merges into thirty-five square kilometres of continuous callowland. Each breeding bird is within calling distance of the next; the pollen of each flower, grass and sedge is within an insect's flight or wind-borne distance from the next; the seeds of each plant find an ideal niche close by; and aquatic life exists in the hundreds of kilometres of connected corridors of drainage ditches. Moreover, if this continuity of habitat cannot be visualised in summer, then the floods, which cover the whole area at some time during the winter, confirm it.

A place among wetlands of the world

In the works of nineteenth century writers the River Shannon brought to mind other European rivers. To H.D.Inglis in 1832 views of the mile-wide callows between Portumna and Meelick (almost a century before these were embanked by the Shannon Scheme) "brought

forcibly back to my recollection the banks of the Guadalquiver between Seville and Cadiz", now one of Europe's finest National Parks, in Spain. Robert Kane, in 1846, considered that if the lands along the Shannon, both above and below Lough Derg, were drained they might be a suitable place for as great a flax industry as alongside some of the rivers which flowed into the Baltic (15). Some parallels with the Callows can, in fact, be seen in recent ecological writings about 900 square kilometres of fen and floodplain grassland in the Biebrza valley (which flows into the Baltic via the Wista River in Poland), although the scale is clearly different: specialist holidays; initial emphasis on birdlife, although vegetation, hydrology and all other aspects of the ecosystem are thought to be equally important; the hope that increased attention, both general and academic, will persuade the authorities to grant it greater conservation status. Neglect of hay making is thought to be the greatest threat there (16).

African savannah grasslands were even brought to mind briefly by an angler sailing downriver from Shannon Harbour in 1845. This was, perhaps, not such a fanciful idea because, in April 1992, two Botswanans thought the scene from their Bed & Breakfast in Shannonbridge, looking north to the expansive Clonburren callows, lacked only giraffe to remind them of home (Illus. 1.3)

Today the Shannon Callows can take their place among the few remaining areas of lowland wet grassland in this part of Europe where productive farming and a vibrant, diverse wildlife co-exist. The others also have collective names, unified by floods: the Blackwater Callows in Co. Waterford; the Derwent Ings in Yorkshire; the Somerset

Levels; the Ouse Washes and Nene Washes of East Anglia; the Amberley Wildbrooks in Sussex; the Ince Flashes in Lancashire; the Ken-Dee Marshes in Southern Scotland; and the Marston Meadows in Staffordshire. Each of these places is different, unique in its combination of human and natural history. Their fortunes are comprehensively and vividly described in *'Taming the Flood'* (17). The Ouse Washes easily top the list as far as size is concerned at two thousand five hundred hectares. So the Callows are the most extensive and this is one of their greatest assets from a nature conservation point of view.

Nature conservation in Europe, Ireland, the Midlands, and the Callows

Many people do not need a reason to conserve nature. To argue the case to the 'non-converted' requires a complex philosophy, nicely expounded in 'Why Conserve Nature ?'(18). Esoterically, everyone would agree that to deface a Michelangelo painting is vandalism. "Why are we not so sensitive when a unique ecosystem is destroyed ? Is it not also a work of art ?" More practically, the premise of nature conservation is that to retain the varied nature of wild species of flora and fauna, plants and animals, on this earth is to benefit human life. The more inhospitable the earth becomes for all species of life, the more inhospitable it becomes for human life. One of the reasons why this is so is described as "exceedingly straightforward" in the *'Irish Red Data Book'* (19), which gives an account of rare plant species in Ireland. Wild species give us a renewable resource - fisheries, game and forestry - the first two have always been outstanding on the Shannon.

All agricultural plants and animals have been bred from wild stock in the past and, in the case of plants, need a continuous input of genes from relatives in the wild. There is a story of a plant-breeder in Britain who returns to a field of wild grasses on the Somerset Levels, from where he had been collecting seeds for an important and long-running agricultural plant breeding programme, only to find the field ploughed and the source of his genetic experiments gone. The Callows have a full range of wild grasses of agricultural use. The substance of most medicines came originally from wild plants and a suprising number still depend on plants which cannot or have not yet been cultivated. Who can know which wild species we will need in the long future of Mankind on earth ? The Callows have a great store of wild plants. 'Lusmagh' means, after all, 'the plain of the healing herbs.' Will the Marsh Cudweed of the Callows be used again to stem the flow of blood from a carpenter's wound as it did at the turn of the nineteenth century ? (20) In Britain in 1899 salicylic acid was apparently obtained from Meadowsweet, surely the most commonplace plant on the Callows, and used in the manufacture of asprin. The roots of Valarian are still used in some brands of proprietary medicine (17).

Natural systems are an indicator of human environmental quality. For instance, the quality of water for human use can be assessed by looking at the plants and invertebrates that can survive in it. And who can deny that the grasslands of the Callows, consisting of wild plant species, flooded each winter and remaining moisture-rich in summer, if less productive, consume less fossil energy than the ploughed, highly fertilised, emerald upland fields of artificially-bred grasses ? Habitats which are managed by man so that human endeavours co-exist with a healthy and diverse nature are sustainable in the long term. A policy for nature conservation in Ireland is set out in *"Our Natural Heritage"* (21).

Finally, very many people get pleasure from contact with nature, and this is where the global scale contracts to the local scale. The Callows are part of the unique natural landscape of the Midlands to which visitors are being successfully attracted in recent years. The spin-offs of 'green tourism', although not always living up to promises of great

prosperity for everyone, nevertheless are an asset to an area.

The European Community has its regulations with regard to nature conservation and each country must maintain its own diversity of wildlife (Chapter 7) not knowing how things will go elsewhere. Ireland has the Wildlife Act (1976). Thus, the Opposite-leaved Pondweed (*Groenlandia densa*), a very geometric plant of clear freshwater and estuaries, is widespread in Europe and Britain but declining. It is listed on the Irish Flora Protection Order (1987) because it has been seen at only four places recently, one of them on the Callows. Wetlands are among the most diverse of natural habitats and

Illus. 1.4 Victoria Lock by Anne O'Connell 1992

Travelling downriver, the passage through Victoria Lock heralds a startling contrast in the Callows landscape, and the sense of space is enormous. The lock was newly constructed during the mid-nineteenth century navigation works and on the cast-iron bollards is moulded: SHANNON COMMISSIONERS 1844

Ireland has been particularly well-endowed with these. Central Ireland has a disproportionate share of wetlands, within the great shallow hollow of the catchment of the River Shannon. Even with reference only to wintering waterbirds the 'Irish Wetlands Survey' (22) documents four major freshwater sites and over one hundred subsidiary sites within the catchment. Within their thirty-five square kilometres the Callows house a most diverse array of species. This is partly because of their size - extra homes for species invariably occur as the area of a habitat increases, and birds especially find the space for large populations to exist (Chapter 5). The diversity is partly due to the dual seasonal nature of the place. The winter wetland becomes, in summer, a mosaic of interwoven habitats for native species from dryland to open water. But it is mostly due to an unavoidably low intensity of farming which in turn is due to the flooding. This is, however, changing (Chapter 6).

A surge of interest

The rare natural character of the Shannon Callows has been delighting naturalists and frustrating farmers for a long time, but the writing of this book coincides with a surge of interest from many angles. The eye of tourism is beginning to focus on the Callows. Biological research workers have realised the significance of a relatively undisturbed wetland ecosystem for study. Ireland's first globally endangered bird, the Corncrake, is coming under great scrutiny on the Callows, which may be its saviour. European Community funds, if the Irish Government so wishes, are available to be directed towards the Callows' farmers in recognition of the temperamental but biologically invaluable fields which they work (Chapter 7).

A place between the Burren and the bogs

A book about just thirty-five square kilometres out of eighty-four thousand in Ireland may seem optimistic. The following pages, however, are designed to illustrate the unexaggerated fact that the Callows are probably the most diverse and lively few hectares in the country. The bogs in the Midlands and the Burren in Co. Clare are well-known examples of fascinating habitats. In many ways they are at opposite ends of a wild and wonderful ecological spectrum between which lie the Callows.

Bogs are soft and very wet, acidic and fed solely by rainwater. They produce a characteristic collection of wildlife-forms and preserved in the layers of peat is an irreplaceable record of past life in the form of pollen grains and other fossils. Present-day human activity on a conserved bog consists only of visiting tourists and ecologists.

The limestone rock, thin soils and crevices on which much of the Burren's outstandingly beautiful flora exists, is a mixture of hard and dry, and excessively damp habitats - calcareous with a high proportion of bare rock. It produces a truly unique flora and fauna, and on its surface are relics of ancient human activity preserved because they are built of stone. Present-day human activity over much of the Burren rocks consists of extensive rough grazing and the ubiquitous tourists and ecologists.

Illus. 1.5 The hidden mouth of the Little Brosna from Victoria Lock by Lorraine Francis 1991

The callows of the Little Brosna provide the "hub of waterbird activity in Ireland" with a greater variety and numbers of migratory winter waterfowl and wading birds than any inland site. In this picture, looking east from the quay at Victoria Lock, the Little Brosna callows open out and stretch four miles beyond the narrow passage between trees slightly right of centre on the horizon.

The Callows are seasonally wet and dry, partly fed by unlimited nutrient and silt-rich river water and springs. Hectare by hecatre - in terms of cattle, grasses, flowers, the birds and invertebrates - the Callows support an immense amount of life throughout the year. They are an agricultural land and almost every square metre features importantly in the lives of the many hundreds of farmers who own them.

The premise of the book

In describing the total character of the Callows it is the premise of this book that this character is worth keeping and worth experiencing. The author is not a farmer so the apparent bias towards the wildlife and the natural environment in the book should be seen in this light. Chapter 5, on farming the Callows, is a product of some first hand conversations and second-hand reports and it is hoped that the Callows it describes are the Callows the farmers know. It is the intention that the farmer who knows his own callow will be able to view the whole Callows. Visitors who are attracted to the Callows by promotional literature, those who chance upon or sail past the Callows, and those who return regularly to experience the nature of the Callows, must remember that the nature they have come to see inhabits farmers' fields. Research workers, adding detail to any aspect of the Callows environment and using them as an 'open air laboratory', will need to take in the total character.

Finally, those in positions to make decisions on the future of the Callows should be aware of all the complex strands which make up this particular aspect of a complex River system and realise that the Callows are truly unique in Europe.

Journey downriver between the Callows in late 1980s

The Callows open out immediately below Athlone town onto Golden Island and Big Meadow. For a mile or so downstream, on the western bank, the boundary between callow and non-callowland is at its least distinct. Higher-than-normal floods quickly transform the callows to once-normal pre-1845 levels, flooding present day roads and homes, but sparing the well-placed cottages on the rocky townland of Carrickynaghtan. Long Island, is never completely submerged, and tapers to a low-lying point, opposite expansively-level, fenced pastureland at the mouth of the River Boor (flowing on the border between Co. Offaly and Westmeath). The peaty meadows at Clonown (Callowbeg) have a mile-long frontage to the river, and are dissected by a 'canal'. The Curraghboy River follows a narrow course through bog, and the callows at its mouth, opposite Inchinalee Island, are dark and peaty with extensive, half-drowned tussocky sedges.

The River becomes wide and the callows narrow, between bogs, until the Pilgrim's Road and the esker hill of Bunthulla overlook the Callows, with spring-line pools beneath. This steep hill provides a gateway to Clonmacnoise, with its great bend in the river and extensive peaty, half-bog half-callows on both sides. A mile of narrow callows lined with half-drowned tussock sedges and bog, connects Clonmacnoise to the wide and contrasting Clonburren callows whose 1837 description -
"very superior meadow loam, good peaty clay soil, with tolerable sandy pasture" - still applies, of course, today. Limestone bedrock is in evidence here, the forested Rocks of Clorhane on the east, and on these Clonburren callows a litter of limestone boulders, never completely submerged.

The wide peninsula of the Cappeletrum callows almost touches Long or Lamb Island which itself reaches Shannonbridge. The River Suck joins the Shannon here, performing a Clonmacnoise-like bend round a bog before doing so. The peat-fired Power Station towers above the meadows on Barannagh callows, which does not deter the Corncrake. The Callows then widen into a complex of silted channels, backwater and meadows at Bishop's Islands on the west and Leitra callows on the east, almost a mile wide. The straightened, peat-laden Blackwater River enters by the shell of Derryholmes House, the old course meandering across low-lying, hedge-lined callows upstream. Even today's floods can surround the hill on which this house stands, which was the site of the most strenuous river-bed excavations in the 1840s. The house was made even lonelier by its facing the start of the longest roadless tract of callowland, on the Galway side.

Not far downstream the Callows open out once more into a four mile stretch of the greatest variety of callows' habitats imaginable, a mile wide in places: past the still-wooded hill at Moystown; Shannon Harbour and the joint-entrance of the Grand Canal and River Brosna; Minus and Bullock 'Islands'; past the twin spires of Banagher; and on to the narrow-necked island of Inishee, specially alive with nesting wading birds in spring. Overgrown islands, grazed islands, quiet shallow backwaters, willow groves, spring-lines and large tracts of hay meadow and pasture on all kinds of callowland. Past the parkland of Shannongrove with the islands always to the south of the modern sailing course. River's edge willows and trees on high ground and embankments still give this stretch, as far as the weir at Meelick and Victoria lock, a 'wooded appearance' commented upon more than a century ago.

Victoria Lock heralds a startling contrast and the sense of space is enormous, with Redwood Bog in Tipperary and the embanked, pumped but still empty 'old callows' stretching over the patchwork of intensive, traditional and abandoned farming on Big and Friar's Islands below Meelick Abbey in Co. Galway. Beyond the green and grazed embankment the many hectares of backwaters, which were part of the pre-1929 braided 'old course' of the Shannon below the rapids at Meelick, contain outstandingly varied aquatic flora. The Little Brosna River enters here but the feeding haven of thousands of winter wildfowl, which stretches four miles to the east, is obscured by a narrow neck between tree-lined bogs.

The west bank of the river along the six miles to Portumna is mostly lined with tall reeds and some willows. Thus the view of the 'old callows' is denied, just as the view of the river from the embankment is also denied. These callows, before the embanking of the river in 1929, were the widest and most 'interminable' of the whole Middle Shannon and are still empty of any buildings. The callows on the Tipperary side, bounded first by bog and then by hills, are often very wet in summer due to the rise of Lough Derg in connection to the Adrnacrusha Hydro-electric Power Station.

CHAPTER 2

"hemmed in by soft glacial deposits and bog"

The Making of the Callows

White Marl

In many drainage ditches on the Callows, and indeed on the banks of the River in places, a creamy white clay can be seen contrasting very sharply with the black peat which rests over it. This is white marl. Under the Callows the white marl is ubiquitous and it is turned up during the dredging of drains. In places, a small portable soil sampler will encounter this marl at a depth of less than 10 cm, and it is probably never more than 300 cm below the surface of the Callows. White marl is almost pure lime (calcium carbonate) and as such it was seen as a valuable manure for improving the 'upland' (ie non- callow) soils. An intensive survey of the whole Callows in 1838 (1), for the purpose of evaluating the land prior to the great navigational and drainage improvements at that time, recorded the presence of white marl as a valuable asset of the callow concerned. No information can be found of any direct use of these marls under the Callows. But in 1801 (2) the presence of 'marles . . . or clays of calcareous quality' in the west part of

Illus. 2.1 White marl under black peat by Anne O'Connell 1992

White Marl is also called 'lake marl', 'Chara marl', or 'shell marl' and is seen here on the sides of a Callows drain, contrasting sharply with the black fen peat above it. The marl underlies all of the Callows and also the adjacent bogs and is evidence that a post-glacial lake of lime-rich water existed here about 9000 years ago - the so-called extended Lough Ree-Derg.

King's County (Co. Offaly) was missed. On closer examination it will be found that this marl often is full of certain species of small snail shells. These tell us that the marl was laid down at the end of the Ice Age in a freshwater lake under conditions which now prevail in the Arctic. The marl is often called 'lake-marl'.

The Ice Age

The events leading up to the Ice Age in Ireland, its progress, its final ending and the subsequent development of eskers, bogs and woodland in the Midlands are well-documented elsewhere (3). The Callows, too, were formed during this ten thousand year blip in Earth's history.

During the period 25 to 2 million years ago the main drainage system of Ireland was probably already established. Part of this, in the centre, was on a great plain of Carboniferous Limestone and may have been shaped by a gentle down-warping of these rocks. Thus the great hollow of the Shannon catchment existed in the centre of Ireland before the Ice Age began, and some of the large lakes, such as Lough Ree, were also in existence. Much of the drainage must have been underground, through the fissures and tunnels of limestone, not unlike today's east Co. Clare where rivers fall from their sandstone hills to disappear under the limestone. The Ice Age sealed most of this leaky surface with a waterproof clay under the ice-sheets and paved the way for the Shannon and its tributaries to flow overground and, in its middle section, to start the formation of the Callows. Some of the drainage into the Shannon and Suck Rivers is still by underground streams (4).

During the Ice Age, from 1.7 million to 10 thousand years ago, this area of the Midlands was covered by thick sheets of ice which stretched indefinitely to the north and ended a number of miles south. Fluctuations in temperature from very cold to quite cold meant that the ice front advanced and retreated. As the ice retreated it left a bare landscape of sands, gravels and boulders crushed and broken by the weight of the ice and the freezing temperatures. Among the most obvious and impressive glacial features left behind are eskers (or esker ridges). These are long winding ridges of glacial sands and gravels which formed in tunnels beneath the ice through which meltwater transported and deposited debris. When the last of the ice finally disappeared these ribbon-like deposits were exposed and the sides, no longer held within the confines of the ice tunnel, slumped and collapsed to give the rather pointed shape we see today.

A typical esker runs along the northern edge of the Little Brosna callows. A great deal of this has been quarried for the valuable lime-rich material it yields for use in the concrete-making business, making ephemeral habitats for hole-nesting Sand Martins (Illus. 2.2) and lime-loving plants. Another, more intact, esker adjoins the Callows on the approaches to Clonmacnoise, continues down to Shannonbridge, is crossed by the River and continues on deep into the heart of East Galway. Eskers have played a large part in the past development and present character of the Callows. Other eskers in the region are shown on Map 3.

An island-studded lake

With the disappearance of the ice-sheet from Ireland meltwater gathered in hollows in the landscape of eroded rock, dumped glacial sands and eskers. The topography around the Callows was dramatic. The bottom of the post-glacial hollow lies up to twenty metres below the present day Callows. For about five hundred years white shell marl accumulated over a lifeless glacial Blue Clay washed from the bare eskers obliterating and smoothing the chaotic topography. The boundaries of the island-studded lake in the vicinity of the Callows - 'an extended Lough Ree-Derg' (3) - must have looked something like that shown in MAP 3, although the actual area of dry ground in and around this lake would have been a little larger - since then the bogs crept up the sides of the eskers and edges of the lake, and clays, marls and alluvium will have smoothed over some low islands.

The story of the early Callows in an Arctic climate is told in the soft geology beneath the grassland. Research work in 1991 tells the story of the Arctic Little Brosna (5). Ongoing pollen analysis of the fen peats beneath the Callows (the first such investigation on the Callows) will reveal the character of the first fens and swamp forests which followed as the climate improved.

Illus. 2.2 Esker sands.
(Photo: S. Heery)

NO ORDINARY RIVER

"The Shannon in fact has eroded no valley in the middle part of its course. Its gradient (slope) is too flat and its flow too slow to mould the landscape. It contrives to flow south as a sort of moving lake, hemmed in by nothing but soft glacial deposits and bog."
1985 (15)

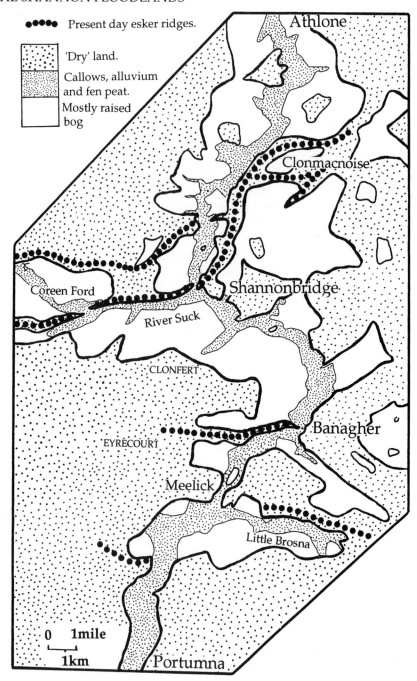

●●●●● Present day esker ridges.

'Dry' land.

Callows, alluvium and fen peat.

Mostly raised bog

Athlone

Clonmacnoise

Coreen Ford

Shannonbridge

River Suck

CLONFERT

EYRECOURT

Banagher

Meelick

Little Brosna

0 1mile

1km

Portumna

MAP 3:   The Callows between the Bogs - the post-glacial lake and present-day esker ridges.

With the disappearance of the ice from Ireland, meltwater gathered in hollows in eroded rock, dumped glacial sands, and eskers. The Shannon was a slow moving lake between Lough Ree and Lough Derg.

The boundaries of this island-studded lake must have looked something like this. Dry ground (lightly stippled) is mostly based on Freeman (1969); the boundary of the Callows (densely stippled) is taken from a satellite picture of the Callows at very high flood. The rest of the 'lake' (white) is now mostly raised bog.

The story of the early Little Brosna callows (12)

The original valley. After the retreat of the ice of the last glaciation the Midlands were left incised with huge valleys, much deeper than today, separated by eskers and piles of glacial drift. The valley floors were covered with gravel and boulder-clay (13). Drainage was very bad under these conditions and most valleys were filled with meltwater. This means that what today are the callows of the Little Brosna valley was part of a lake that covered a large part of the Shannon catchment, including many of the areas now covered by bogs.

Early sedimentation, the lake clays. The climate was much colder than today: the underground was permanently frozen (14); vegetation was scarce; and evaporation rates were low. This meant that erosion was high in the Little Brosna catchment, especially in the Slieve Bloom mountains. The coarser sands and gravels were left behind upstream but the finer sand, silt and clay settled only where the flow was slowest - in the lake. The lake quickly filled up with these fine sediments (a) (Illus. 2.3) to a thickness of over thirteen metres in the centre. The sand layers, coarse at the edge (b) and finer in the centre (c), were caused by small landslides of saturated material flowing over the frozen ground

A large drop in the lake level - a thin layer of sand. This period of constant quiet sedimentation was ended when the lake-level dropped dramatically. The abruptness of this change is witnessed by a thin layer of sand (only about 3 cm) which is found almost everywhere in the valley (d). The abrupt drop in lake-level might have had two causes: a break in a natural dam downstream in the Shannon valley; and a decrease in the amount of water entering the lake. The sand layer was formed as the water flowed away, taking with it the finer silt and clays. A gradual change in climate allowed vegetation to cover the catchment which, along with a disappearance of the permafrost, prevented the severe erosion leading to a sharp decrease in the amount of sediment entering the lake.

Changing climate - the lake marl deposition. On top of the thin sand layer a completely different sediment is found: the lake marls (shell marls), white to light brown marls which consist almost entirely of calcareous material (e). Embedded in this marl is a variety of well-preseved remains of animals and plants which lived at this time: bivalve shells (cockles, mussels etc); snails; parts of insects; ostracods (shrimps etc); diatoms (miscroscopic algae); *Chara* (calcareous algae); and roots, stems and seeds. Lake marl was formed in shallow water which was high in calcium due partly to the growing aquatic plant-life taking carbon dioxide from the water, mostly during the summer (see 'recycled lime', below). This seasonality of marl formation caused laminae (or stripes) in the marl rather like tree rings record each season's growth. Interestingly, some layers in the marls consist entirely of shells, mostly in the upper parts, possibly as a result of temporary erosion washing away the finer marl.

The end of the lake 9,000 years ago. When the water levels got too low for marl deposition, quite abruptly again, the lake turned into a fen-sedge/reedswamp with some marsh forest, and peat development started (f). The growth rate of peat was highest at the edges of the valley due to a continuous supply of nutrient-rich seepage water. At some places the callows accumulation of peat was high enough for bogs to develop. The small peat dome in the Clongowna callow (g) is probably a remainder of such a bog which has been cut-away in centuries past.

The impact of humans - so far. The last stage of sedimentation in the Little Brosna callow is caused by humans: forests were cut down; lands were cultivated; erosion and run-off increased (fewer trees to use and hold the rainwater). This led to an increase in flooding intensities and sedimentation in today's callows. The peat in the bottom parts of the floodplain are covered with fine silt and clayey silt changing the soil and vegetation. Bordering the river raised levées consist of fine silts and sands with some layers of gravel and coarse sand. Sedimentation continues today during floods, although at a fairly low rate. This sediment input is a source for the nutrients that makes the plant-life here different from that in most of the Shannon Callows.

Recycled lime

The deposition of white marl on the bed of this lake was a recycling of the lime deposited in warm seas 340 millions of years previously in the form of Carboniferous Limestone of the Central Plain of Ireland. Water can dissolve calcium carbonate (lime) and the post-glacial waters of Central Ireland were very rich in dissolved lime. The amount of lime held depends on the levels of carbon dioxide (CO_2) in the water. Thus, if carbon dioxide is somehow taken out then the water cannot hold so much lime. Calcium carbonate is precipitated out of the water in the form of creamy white particles, called tufa or travertine. There are many ways this can come about and some of them are still working on the Callows today.

When water emerges from a deep spring differences in air pressure causes a loss of CO_2 and creamy white 'tufa' is left. Such a spring exists near Shannon Harbour where the water emerges from a hill of bedrock Limestone and the stems of the Long-stalked Yellow Sedge and Watercress are tufa-covered. Stoneworts are an unusual group of aquatic non-flowering plants, related to Algae. Some of them, notably *Chara* spp., are lime-loving and their system of photosynthesis means, as the name 'stonewort' implies, that their stems become encrusted with lime. White marl is sometimes called *Chara* marl for this reason. Such *Chara* spp. can be found today on the Callows in drains and backwaters where clear, peat-free water lies over white marl, and where water emerges from permanent or even temporary springs.

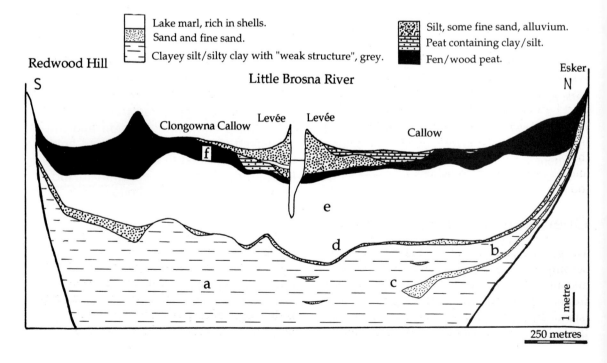

Illus. 2.3 The soft geology beneath the Little Brosna callows

Lake marl, rich in shells.
Sand and fine sand.
Clayey silt/silty clay with "weak structure", grey.

Silt, some fine sand, alluvium.
Peat containing clay/silt.
Fen/wood peat.

Redwood Hill

S

Little Brosna River

Esker

N

Clongowna Callow

Levée Levée

Callow

f

e

d

b

a

c

1 metre

250 metres

The north side of the Little Brosna Callows have such drains. The wonderfully clear depths of the backwaters and drains on the embanked side of the River at Meelick (see Chapter 3) are other places where lime-encrusted stoneworts grow in abundance and variety.

An increase in water temperature can make lime precipitate out, and the resulting loss of water to evaporation along with increased plant activity, using CO_2 during growth, accelerates the deposition of white marl. The lime-rich water was an ideal medium for the growth of snails which utilised lime in their shell and returned it when they died. White marl is sometimes called 'shell marl'. The marls under the Callows have not yet been studied but a complete sequence in Co. Down (6) reveals that the fossil snail shells at the base are those species which now live in the Arctic, and those in the upper parts are species which now live in present day Norway, south of the Arctic circle. The climate was becoming warmer. White marl is being formed on the bed of some Irish lakes today, notably Lough Carra in the Corrib catchment. At Lough Derg in 1864 (7) it was noted that 'an inexhaustible supply of unctuous marl is to be had merely by dredging the bottom of the lake'. Unfortunately, peat silt and other pollution probably obliterates this today.

Open water and boggy wetland

The gradual return to warmer conditions was accompanied by the recolonisation of plants and animals to Ireland. The lake was colonised from the perimeter and the edges of the esker islands by plant species which are familiar in the Callows today. Plants requiring no land at all to establish themselves, such as the free-floating Duckweeds and Frogbit must have made their way across the lakes. The remains of floating plants such as Pondweeds and Water Lilies, plants of shallow water such as Bulrushes and Reeds, plants of wet peaty ground such as sedges, and other Callows plants such as Marsh Marigold, Marsh Cinqufoil, Cuckoo Flower, Meadowsweet, Marsh Pennywort, Grass of Parnassus and others have been found as fossils in marls elsewhere in Ireland as well as peats which overly them. Accumulation of the debris from these plants, especially Phragmites, the common reed, began to form peat. This process is easily seen in the small enclosed backwaters of the 'old course of the Shannon' at Meelick, where old broken stems of reed lie for years on the bed. The sequence of events subsequent to the formation of the first fen peat in these lakes is that eventually the surface was high enough to prevent the plant species from taking nutrients via the roots from the mineral floor beneath the peat. Most plants need this sort of nutrient supply, but *Sphagnum* moss can thrive without. It can obtain enough nutrients from the rainwater which it stores and attracts like a sponge. In this very special environment *Sphagnum* moss grew upwards and outwards from the lake to develop into the great raised bogs which surround the Shannon Callows today.

The River Shannon now flows in broad curves through a distinctly Central Irish landscape of bogs, eskers and callows. The Shannon basin might be called the type locality of these landscape features because the Irish language is the origin of each of these words (bog = bogach, esker = eiscir, callow = caladh)

Which came first: the bog or the Callows ?

For a significant part of its course the Shannon Callows lie against high ground, with bog on one side only (Map 3). As the bogs grew, a watercourse was maintained between the outflow of Lough Ree and the expanse of water arrested in the south by the natural dams at Killaloe and at Meelick (where the River ran even before the start of the Ice Age)(8). *Sphagnum* will not grow in running water, so the watercourse did not become overwhelmed. *Sphagnum* will only grow in acid conditions fed by rainwater. At the edges of raised bogs there is usually an area kept free from *Sphagnum* growth by contact with the mineral soil, lime-rich springs and upwelling groundwater. The course of the Shannon settled to run close by the edges of the lake surrounded by very wide areas of fenland.

It is interesting to speculate that a somewhat random spreading of glacial material made the Shannon run along the western side of the esker ridges at Clonmacnoise rather than draining to the east. A very different river course would now be present and the Callows would be somewhere to the east. The landscape around Birr might have included wide expanses of Shannon Callows, and the confluence of the Suck and Shannon might have been at Shannon Harbour, where the Brosna River joins today. Before arterial drainage of the River Brosna the yearly Shannon floods reached far upriver. During the thousands of years of bog development at Pollagh Bog (now extinct beside the lines of the River Brosna, the Grand Canal and the old Clara-Banagher railway) changes in the regime of flooding from the Shannon interrupted the growth to create fen peat lenses sandwiched between *Sphagnum* peat (10).

Fen woodland

To reconstruct an ancient landscape in the mind is an inexact exercise of informed speculation, even when evidence abounds in research work. About seven thousand years ago woodland grew on the fen peat on either side of the watercourse, the reborn Shannon. The climate was more 'favourable' than it had been in the past or would be in the future, and the great raised bogs had not yet begun to grow in earnest. The River was probably smaller than at present, rainfall was less, flooding was less. The extended Lough Ree-Derg had been infilling with the remains of plants for 2000 years. Looking down from the hill on which Banagher stands today the canopy of this woodland (perhaps oak-alder-elm) would have stretched like a billowy sea, and the Shannon was a willow-, alder-, birch-lined water course, perhaps with extensive areas of grasses, such as Reeds or Reed Sweetgrass, emerging from permanent shallow water (Illus. 2.4). Fossil pollen evidence trapped in the peats of the bogs tell us that during the next couple of thousand years the alder became much more common - the climate was becoming wetter and cooler. Clonfert Bog, Blackwater and all the other Bogs began to grow in earnest, the fen peats around the River were wetter and flooding more extensive.

Extensive areas of woodland which 'have their feet in water' are rare in Europe today but those that do exist are generally made up of the trees Alder and/or various types of Willow, and Birch (9). Seven species of Willow grow on the Callows today. Alder grows on wet peat which is not too acid and would have found a home on the fen peats along the River. There is little evidence on, or under, the Callows grasslands today as to what these swamp and fen woodlands were like. Tree remains under the bogs are common and well-known for two reasons. Firstly, they were overwhelmed and sealed from air by a permanently wet *Sphagnum* blanket. Secondly, harvesting of the bogs has uncovered these remains. The fallen trees of the Callows woodland were exposed to the air during times of low flood and decomposition was more complete, especially on the higher parts. If any tree remains exist under the central parts of the Callows they lie hidden two metres under the grassland.

Most lie hidden, but not all. A section exposed on the river bank on Bishop's Islands shows substantial red-tinged logs of Birch with bark intact lying in a peat containing the light golden brown stems of thick reeds, the level water of the summer Shannon suggesting that this existed in a hollow. Birch was a common tree in the in-filling post-glacial lakes before the invasion of *Sphagnum* and the establishment of bog (10). By the banks of the early Shannon, the increased rainfall that caused bog growth sealed this Birch under almost a metre of alluvium. A somewhat different scenario existed at the centre of the bend of the River at Clonmacnoise. Here three metres of peat grew almost to a Bog, away from the influence of River floods, but also supported Birch in the late stages. Even today little alluvium has reached this level (Illus. 2.5).

Close to the buried birch stumps, not one mile upriver, a very small living Alderwood, whose damp barks are clothed in lichens, gives only the very faintest hint of what part of these woodlands were like. These Alders survive on a (hopefully) undrainable, permanently wet upwelling of water from the bog behind. In July, a luxuriant growth of six foot high Meadowsweet, Gypsywort and, in patches, Nettles grow from a ground layer of Floating Sweetgrass and Creeping Bentgrass (11). The Alders of this wood barely reach six inches in diameter. In the National Museum we find a shield one metre in diameter worked from a slice taken from a trunk of a well-grown Irish forest Alder:
"Only in some remote parts of Europe can we recapture something of the vanished dignity of the Irish forests." (3)

Illus. 2.4 A reminder of what the original swamp woodland must have been like - Scrubby Islands, Meelick. (Photo: S. Heery)

Increased alluvial deposition

The present day topography, dimensions, and pattern of soils on the Callows is a result of a period, starting about 4000 years ago when Ireland became wetter and cooler, causing more erosion of uplands, flooding and deposition of alluvium on the River floodplain. This was the time when the bogs made a spurt of growth upwards and outwards until, at the present edge of the Callows, the seasonal flooding stopped the growth of rain-fed *Sphagnum*. Forest clearance was accelerated at this time (the Bronze Age) due to the efficient use of tools, and also contributed to alluvial floodplain development. This was the case 1600 years ago on the River Boyne, later or

earlier in other catchments depending on the circumstances (3). In the centre of the Little Brosna callows alluvium covers fen peat to a depth of almost two metres and continues to be brought down dramatically from the Slieve Bloom. On the outer parts, however, the fen peat (much diminished and humified) is still pure and receives no alluvium. The zone of deposition has always been concentrated in the central parts of the Callows.

The Shannon River above Meelick however does not have the same erosion hinterland. Where are the mountains ? Much of the alluvial deposits must be reworked fine silts and clays from the eskers. Sand grains of quartz, sorted by the river from the chaotic mixture of esker sands, are prominent in the levée at Clonmacnoise. Are the high banks of alluvium of Bullock Island a result of the prehistorical Brosna River (a tributary of which drains from the Slieve Bloom mountains) emptying its load into the Shannon? Similarly, are Bishop's Islands somehow connected to the confluence of the River Suck ? The present day alluvial regime has only just begun to be studied. Banks of fine sand were noticed at Bishop's Islands after arterial drainage of the Cloonascragh River, a few miles away on the River Suck.

The post-1960s Shannon carries a new and lighter sediment - peat 'silt', a product of the large scale harvesting of the surrounding bogs. There is serious problem of this peat settling on the River bed and in the basin of Lough Derg. But it also invades the Callows habitats, notably the reedbeds. Sometimes, under certain conditions of flooding, the peat 'silt' spreads itself over some of the Callows grasslands.

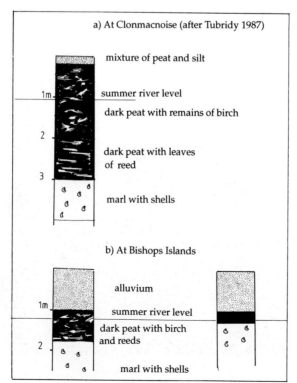

Illus. 2.5 Cross-sections, showing river alluvium over fen peat with Birch over white lake shell marl. (the Clonmacnoise section is redrawn from "the Heritage of Clonmacnoise" by Tubridy and Jeffrey (eds) 1987, with permission)

a) At Clonmacnoise (after Tubridy 1987)

mixture of peat and silt

1m — summer river level

dark peat with remains of birch

2

dark peat with leaves of reed

3

marl with shells

b) At Bishops Islands

alluvium

1m — summer river level

dark peat with birch and reeds

2

marl with shells

A river floodplain unique in Europe

Today (as in the past) the Shannon is a tranquil river compared to the rivers of Europe which emanate from the Massif Central of France, or the Alps. It is a clean river compared to those that pass through the cities of Europe on their way to the Netherlands and the North Sea. No shifting banks of sand, no snow melt to fill its banks in spring and little industrial chemical pollution. Plant-life on the middle Loire in France has to cope with desert-like dryness after being inundated by floods which rise five metres each year. The Shannon is the largest and longest river in a part of Europe with the most oceanic climate, with an even annual distribution of rainfall, and its catchment is the least industrial, and the least populated of all large rivers in Europe.

Illus. 2.6 Tranquil backwaters near the Meelich pumphouse, in winter.

Illus. 3.1 Flooding on the
Callows just south of Athlone
in September 1985.
(Photo: Irish Times).

CHAPTER 3

"the acres that feed the winter swans"

Flooding on the Callows

Inevitable flooding

The annual transformation of the River Shannon, from placid river between green farmland to a lake-like expanse, with all the subtle combinations as the waters encroach and recede, cannot fail to make an impression. Most first-time visitors will not have seen anything like it, and those closest to the Callows, the farmers, have their own impressions. It is not surprising that the River floods and that so far it has not been tamed. A scale model of the Callows landscape, including the tributaries of the Shannon, would show that the analogy of the badly functioning gutter (l) is a most apt one. The amount of water flowing under Athlone bridge (in 1818 it was "as transparent as the Rhone at Geneva, but not so blue" (2)) during the winter simply exceeds the capacity of the river channel downstream. The outer limit of floodwater, spreading across the fields, is contained not by a man-made bank, but simply stops at a point determined by a shallow topography.

The situation is compounded by incredibly low gradients in this middle section, and by waters from the Suck, Brosna and Little Brosna Rivers. The situation is made worse by the six kilometre bottleneck between Banagher and Meelick (3). Other constrictions in the flow occur where the River crosses the eskers at Shannonbridge and Banagher, where Callows are non-existent. These three places were probably the cause of the original post-glacial lake damming and so provide a link with the past.

Lough Ree inflow/outflow 1965

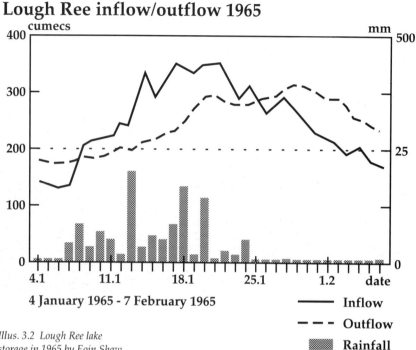

4 January 1965 - 7 February 1965

— Inflow
- - - Outflow
▨ Rainfall

Illus. 3.2 Lough Ree lake storage in 1965 by Eoin Shaw

In 1965, water flowing into Lough Ree after heavy rain quickly reached high levels and remained high, gradually filling the lake. Water flowing out onto the Callows south of the lake increased only slowly and was always lower than that entering the lake. Flooding on the Callows was less than it could have been. It was, however, more prolonged as it was released slowly from the lake - water in winter cannot be made to disappear into thin air.

A NEW URGENCY

"The River takes on a new urgency as it leaves Banagher. Gone are the low-lying fields, the cattle drinking on its banks, the slow lazy river twisting and turning this way and that. The flow (speed) of the river increases, confined in narrow channels and divided by many islands. It is this stretch of river between Banagher and Meelick that is responsible in a large degree for the Shannon floods: the fall of the River between Banagher and Meelick is about 2" per mile, whereas from Athlone to Banagher it is only about 1' per mile. At Counsellor's Ford, south of Inishee Island, the great waters of the River are forced through a narow channel less than 500 metres wide." 1987 (24)

Irish summers are certainly not guaranteed to be dry, although surprisingly, the Central Lowlands is the driest area of Ireland (4). The average rainfall at Birr from 1961 to 1990 was only slightly lower in the summer than in winter. Yet in summer, when usually about 97 cubic metres of water per second can flow out of Lough Derg, floods are thankfully rare. In winter the outflow can be about 259 cubic metres per second and floods are inevitable. The difference is due to evaporation. In summer, higher temperatures and growing plants in the whole catchment cause a loss of water to the air (evapotranspiration). At the end of the summer the water underground has usually been depleted. The floods wait until the autumn rains have restored this. Just as the garden lawn in autumn and winter never dries out, almost all the rain that falls in winter finds its way to the River, little is lost to the air. The floods rise inexorably, usually before Christmas, often in November or October.

Lake storage

The amount of water passing down river is called 'flow' (measured in cubic metres of water per second - cumecs). As flow increases, so floodwaters rise. The more water which is spread over the Callows, the more gradually and less catastrophically it passes downstream - the Callows are a flood relief system. The large Shannon lakes of Lough Derg, Ree and Allen are used as temporary storage for potential floodwater to great effect. For example, although 90 cumecs were entering Lough Allen during times of heaviest rainfall in February 1990, only half that amount was ever passing out into the Shannon. Similarly, in January 1965, water flowing into Lough Ree after heavy rain quickly reached high levels and remained high, gradually filling the lake. Water flowing out onto the Callows south of Athlone increased slowly and was always lower than that entering the Lake (Illus. 3.2). Flooding of the Callows was less than it could have been (5). It was, however, more prolonged as it was released slowly from the lake - water in winter cannot be made to disappear into thin air. Recent suggestions have been made that some of the cut-away bogs alongside the Shannon may be used as new flood storage areas in the same way.

Summer flooding

The images of men trying to scythe and save hay which was flooded at Clonmacnoise in 1830 (6), and moving haycocks to higher ground by boat at Little Portland in 1879 (7), had their modern equivalent in August and September 1985 (Illus. 3.1). Many interests lay claim to the Shannon farming, wildlife conservation, fishing, tourism, navigation, energy production, water supplies, and pollution control. Sometimes these conflict. But, it is agreed, summer flooding of the Callows is in nobody's interest. Even the wildlife and its conservationists will say that flooding after the middle of April is unwanted. The Little Brosna callows were full to the brim in June 1983.

Unpredictable flooding

The only predictable thing about flooding on the Callows is that it has occurred each winter and will occur in the foreseeable future. The extent and duration of each winter's flood is almost entirely at the mercy of the weather. In

Engraved by J. Greig, from a Drawing by Geo. Petrie, for the Excursions through Ireland.

BANAGHER,

KING'S COUNTY.

HARDSHIP

"On these lowlands, at the base of a limestone gravel hill near Clonmacnoise, I saw men (Autumn 1930) stripped nearly to the hips, actually mowing the long grass as it stood full two thirds under water, whilst others dragged it out and carried it on their shoulders to the banks to be dried." (6)

"I have seen the Shannon in real flooded state...the bankside farmers lost their identity and some of their flocks. It is a fearful sight. The sluices are opened, the water rises and comes so fast, with everybody helpless until the rains and the running water of enormous volume stops." 1988 (23)

Illus. 3.3 Eel weirs at Banagher in 1820. In 1801, the presence of eel-weirs was blamed for unnecessary flooding upstream. An engraving from Thomas Cromwell's 'Excursions', courtesy of James Scully.

historical accounts flooding which keeps within the confines of the Callows in winter has been hardly worth mentioning. But floods which creep beyond the Callows to inundate roads, houses and more conventional farmland are 'bad floods'. They have occurred throughout the history of the Shannon and are a product of heavy rain, sometimes, as in March 1947 and January 1925, compounded with melting snow (often, of course, the same weather is affecting Britain). The worst flood since records began occurred from 11 October 1954 to 2 January 1955 and more water poured over Parteen Weir than at any time before or since (5). This flood started with 4.2 inches of rain falling in four days, followed by daily rain which included another four inches in five days during November. This was followed, as the headlines of the local Connaught Tribune put it, by "Chaotic Conditions in the Wake of Fierce Storm" on December 11. That night fire, not floods, destroyed the former Bishop's Palace at Clonfert, then occupied by Sir Oswald Mosley, two miles from the Bishop's Islands callows. The Callows lake at that time approached 4,000 hectares surrounded by another 4,000 hectares of waterlogged land.

On 8th December 1954 a woman and her invalid daughter lay in their beds with the Shannon-level already very high and lapping around the walls of their low-beamed, thatched cottage within sight of Banagher. Unbelievably, overnight, the River rose another fourteen inches to surround their beds. Their evacuation by boat was an event repeated throughout the Callows that winter. The hardships of previous floods are largely lost from living memory. In 1873 boats were tied permanently under the beds of still occupied houses in the Clonown

area in case the River rose any more (8). Most of the cottagers who were flooded out in 1954 were relocated by the Government to safer spots, so subsequent bad floods did not affect so many occupied houses. The 1990 flood, whose maximum height at Banagher was eight inches lower than that of 1954, affected houses at Shannon Harbour and near Athlone. In 1990 the river almost over-topped the Shannon Electrification Scheme embankment, the floods in this lower section being higher than in 1954 (5). The embankment has since been raised by a foot in some places.

Four other major floods which cover all the highest levels and flows on record were (5):
1924-25 1 December to 25 January
1959-60 14 December to 17 January
1965-66 4 January to 7 February
1990 14 January to 18 March

Nineteenth century floods, before records began, may well have been just as severe. In the middle of December 1991 the River was still within its banks. At the time of writing, the end of November 1992, the Callows are full to the very brim. The River fell quickly after the severe March flood of 1990, giving a long dry spring and summer with early hay making on the Callows.

'Normal' flooding

The River Shannon does not 'burst its banks'. At some time during the autumn the flood begins to rise: seen first as shining lines picking out the rectangular pattern of drains; then as an advancing floodline whose true position is hidden because the water lies just at the surface between the tufts of grass and sedge. In some parts of the river, the land rises towards the riverbank. The floodwaters creep round this rise, making an island. In a classic river situation this is a 'levée', built up by deposition of sediment each time the river overtops its banks. On the Shannon, they are likely to be partly the result of nineteenth century drainage work. The long and ribbon-like 'levées' on the Little Brosna, and elsewhere, are invaluably remote refuges and feeding areas for the wildfowl and waders which congregate there in winter (Illus. 5.1).

The rise and fall of the River is recorded automatically at key points and also by the more traditional (and sometimes more reliable) method of reading a gauge every morning at 09.00hrs. The Callows fields are flat, with rarely a difference in height of over one metre. Consequently, a small rise in the river-level can flood a large area. The details of each callow are different but the generality is true. At Shannon Harbour the 'normal' summer river-level lies at least half a metre below most of the Callows. But after this has been taken up, a rise of only 30cm makes the difference between one quarter and three quarters of the callows being flooded (9). Therefore most of the floodwaters are shallow and ideal for the wildfowl that feed there. In April the water drains and evaporates off the Callows slowly but steadily and it takes about three weeks for the surface water to disappear once the River has confined itself to its banks. No matter how high the floods have been in April, warm temperatures, evaporation and plant growth usually ensure that most of the Callows are dry by the middle of May.

Trends in flooding

In 1801 the presence of eel-weirs were blamed for unnecessary flooding (Illus. 3.3).

"...near Banagher...these weirs are evidently very injurious to the bottom meadows, and throw up a considerable quantity of backwater." (10)

The floods that travellers saw before 1845 were generally more severe than at present. Floodwater lay longer on the Callows and areas beyond today's limits were annually flooded. Map 4 shows the extent of flooding around Banagher that the Shannon Commissioners found before their recommendations on navigation improvement were implemented. Most of today's Callows could be under water for six months and fields which rarely flood today could be inundated for three months annually (11). The outer limit of this 1839 map was reached during the 1954 floods when the floods reached the road to Clonfert.

Navigation improvements included the removal of 'shoals' of bedrock and esker gravels, some of them ancient fording places of immense historical significance, at White's Ford, Keeloge, Moystown, Derryholmes, Bishop's Islands, Shannonbridge, Devenish Island, the ancient Ford at Snám Dá Éan (Swim two Birds), Bunthulla beneath the great truncated esker at Clonmacnoise, and the west side of Inchinalee Island. The stones left by the riverside now make excellent perches for Common Sandpipers (Illus. 3.4) . In addition, a New Cut was excavated, now a wide, densely wooded channel, at Lusmagh. Another, at Shannonbridge, is now a place to moor hired cruisers. The general level of the River at Clonmacnoise was lowered by over one foot

MAP 4 a, b The Callows in 1838 by Samuel Nicholson 1839, courtesy of Royal Irish Academy.

4 a) Banagher;
4 b) Clonmacnoise.

The maps show the extent of flooding before the 1845 engineering works to improve navigation and drainage. Three broken lines indicate parts of the callows which were: "usually flooded 6 months in a year"; " . . . 3 months in a year; " . . . a shorter period than 3 months in a year".

The maps give fascinating insights into the Callows of the time. There is space for two points only here:

4 a) The towpath of the Grand Canal is extended across a wide and exposed part of the River on a narrow wooden bridge across which the horses walked, towing the passenger barges on the river - precarious arrangement (Delany 1987). The remains of the wooden piles are still visible on both sides of the River.

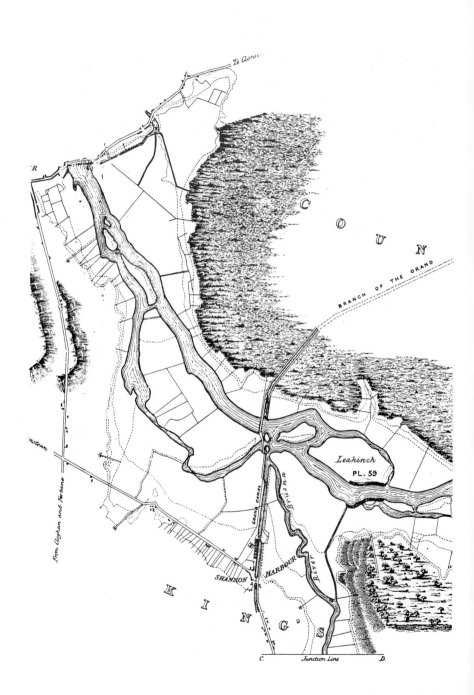

and field drains became more efficient (12).
This initiated changes in the Callows edge
vegetation (see Chapter 4: Tall Sedges). The
effect was particularly noticeable at
Clonmacnoise. The great pre-1845 west-facing
river inlet, seen on Map 4, is today an area of
reedswamp and tall sedges. Similarly, on the
west bank callows, two hectares of tall sedges
and an isolated clump of reeds have replaced
the lake indicated on Nicolson's 1938 map. But
any improvements in conditions for Callows
farming in the good times were swept away
from the minds of proprietors by the inevitable
recurrence of bad floods.

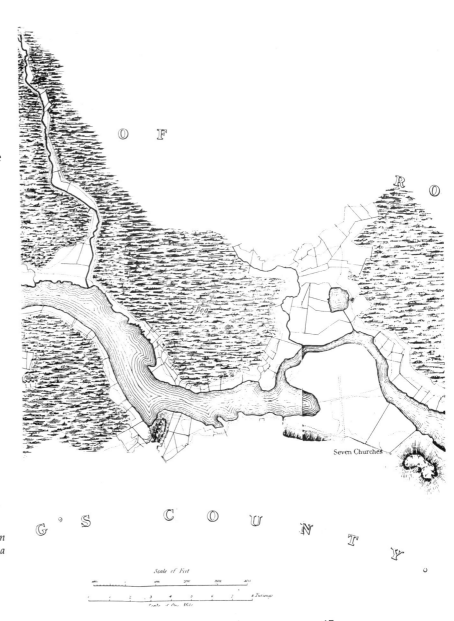

*4 b) The small lake on the
peaty callows opposite
Clonmacnoise was drained
after the navigation works
lowered the summer level of
the River by over one foot.
The relic lake can still be seen
as an area of tall sedges and a
patch of reeds draped with
MARSH PEA and other
flowers, fed by emerging
ground water.*

Illus. 3.4 Stones near Devenish Island. Stones in the River, either dredged up during nineteenth century navigation works, or occuring naturally as esker boulders, are favoured by Common Sandpipers for perches. (Photo: S. Heery)

April - a crucial month

April is a crucial month, when the Callows are in transition from wetland to productive farmland. If the Callows are still wet or flooded at this time the farmers must wait to start their grassland management and the groundnesting wading birds start their cycle of courtship and choice of nest-sites truly wading in a wide land almost devoid of disturbance.

It is often claimed that flooding has been more severe in recent years and this is certainly the case, at least for spring flooding, at one representative Callows site (Shannon Harbour). From 1960 to 1990 it was found that April flooding was more frequent since 1976 than before (13). The hydrology of the Shannon basin is complex and is only now being studied in detail (14) so it is not yet possible to find reasons. Some tributaries have been drained so that all their water passes quickly into the Shannon. Bogs have been drained but this apparently decreases their flooding effects - the peat 'sponge' is no longer saturated and so can absorb rainfall, although they will let their water out over a longer period.

Rain is still the most immediate cause of floods. In April 1991 high floods were the latest, rainfall the highest and temperatures the lowest for the thirty years previous. If anything other than natural causes are to blame for increased flooding then it must be shown that for any given rainfall the chances of flooding has increased. At the Ouse Washes, in England, this has been shown to be the case, although in a much more severe way, to the detriment of both farmers and wildlife. Silt accumulation of the outflow channels and increased drainage of land upstream are the speculated but unconfirmed cause (15).

What is drainage?

"In spite of their inherent richness, many of the wetlands ...have been seen as obstacles to the advancement of agriculture which relies, for most of its economic production, on a very small number of dryland species." (16)

When water lies in the rooting zone of dryland plants their growth is deterred or prevented by chemical reactions in the soil caused mainly by

Illus. 3.5 Shannon Harbour, the Grand Canal, Brosna River and Shannon Callows in 1966. (Photo: courtesy of University College, Dublin.)

lack of oxygen. Wetland plants have adapted ways to deal with this, including storing of their own oxygen. Reeds are masters at this, but all Callows plants which often find their roots in water in March and April have some strategy to deal with it. Floodwater and waterlogged soil in spring delays the start of grassland management because farm machinery and cattle would destroy the field surface and make it unfit for growth even

when dry. Drainage is the permanent lowering of the water under the land. Compared to three hundred years ago, most of Ireland is now drained.

"Drain the Shannon !" means contain the floods between embankments or the banks of a deepened river and draw the water-table down to a respectable depth below the surface of the land. The 3,500 hectares of Callows is not the

47

only, or even primary concern, in this matter. Because of very low gradients in the Shannon catchment a combination of floods and a high water-table along the Shannon and Suck affects not only the Callows but large areas drained by even the smallest of tributaries and streams. An estimated 500,000 hectares are affected or 'damaged' in this way (17).

'Damaged' land is defined by the Office of Public Works as "Wetlands bordering river channels which require lowering of the outfall to carry out drainage for improvement". Some wet grassland is not regarded as 'damaged' because of springs and other groundwater conditions are felt to be responsible for the wetness. The Shannon Callows are regarded at present as 'damaged' land but little is, in fact, known of the presence of springs and seepages which may alter this assessment.

Calls for drainage

"In 1989 we can celebrate 150 years of unsuccessful Shannon drainage, perhaps even issue a stamp portraying Clonown in winter" (8). This describes the frustration of those involved in earning a living from the Callows or have had their property underwater a few times since 1954. In 1835 the Shannon Commissioners were established to prepare detailed plans for both drainage and navigation of the River. The works continued from 1839 to 1846 and during that time expectations were very high for the use of the post-drainage Callows. In 1989 similar (unfulfilled) expectations were being prophesied (by politicians) about the the small but long-awaited navigation works along the River Suck from Shannonbridge to Ballinasloe (18).

GREAT EXPECTATIONS

"The lands hitherto liable to flood by irregular risings of the Shannon but, by improvements of its channel, about to be permanently rendered available to agriculture, amount to 32,500 acres above Limerick." 1846 (25)

Weirs, at Athlone, Meelick and Parteen have some control over water-levels, but cannot prevent high floods. After catastrophic flooding in 1861 a Commission of Enquiry recommended the fitting of sluices to the navigation weir at Meelick. Twenty-two years later (a familiar delay) this was done. The sluiceless navigation weir at Killaloe was blamed for bad flooding above Portumna in 1879 (7). Wonderful coloured lithographs were produced to illustrate the point (Illus. -). Fifty years later the weir was removed during the Shannon Electrification Scheme and sixty years after that a computer study (5) showed that flooding south of Meelick had indeed been somewhat more severe while the weir was in operation.

Illus. 3.6 The Shannon Floods by Henry Trench 1879:

"Heifer and Harvest cart on boat, going for haycocks, and drawn by wire across to landing stage". A scene at Little Portland two miles upriver from Portumna (courtesy of Royal Irish Academy).

This, and two other beautiful coloured lithographs, were produced in a short report aimed at persuading the authorities to remove, or fit sluices to, the weir at Killaloe which was blamed for unnecessary flooding as far back as Meelick. Ironically, the report goes on call for measures to retain floodwater in some circumstances for irrigation:

"Land flooded at a loss in September, which six weeks later, could have been irrigated with profit on November 1".

G.H. Kinahan, an eminent Irish geologist of 'strikingly imposing physique' and a prolific writer, watched and recorded the birds of the Callows while thinking about the persisting problem of floods. In 1882 (19) he concluded that the land had to be protected from: "floods coming down the river; the "backwater' or floods coming up the river; and from upland waters". Upland waters were streams which emerged from the surrounding land without drains to carry them to the river. If these were emerging from the bogs they were thought to "poison the land". One solution was to carry all these upland waters along a canal on the margins of the Callows to a single outfall somewhere downstream. This would have provided us with the legacy of a beautiful habitat for aquatic plants today, but it was never acted upon. Floods coming up or down the river could be, Kinahan suggested, resolved by embankments, erected not too close to the river's edge (where willows would be planted)

Such an embankment was involved when the next dramatic change in flooding on the Callows came with the Shannon Electrification Scheme in 1929 (see below).

A review of the report by the Drainage Commission 1938-40 puts the problem of complete Callows drainage quite clearly. They pointed out that at times of flood five feet of water can cover thousands of acres of Callows (an exaggeration). To confine this volume within the banks of even a widened river channnel would require an impossible amount of deepening. With regard to the other method of confining the floods, embanking, the relative narrowness of the Callows prevents it. The need to be some distance back from the existing river bank, the width of the embankment and adjacent canal, means that its raising would make long stretches of improved callowland very narrow indeed. The cost per acre (including the cost of pumping the improved lands to prevent the water-table from seeping up from the river) would have a poor return.

The floods of 1954-5 prompted the most comprehensive look at the possiblity of drainage of the Shannon. Only five months after these floods had receded Mr Louis Rydell of the US Corps of Engineers, a leading expert on flood control, visited Ireland to advise on "the possibility of dealing effectively and permanently with the periodic flooding in the Shannon Valley". His report was published one year later (20). While accepting, and including, a report by agriculturalists that full total flood relief would enable farmers to carry out a "normal cropping programme" with cash crops and better pasture, L.E.Rydell emphasised the navigation, fisheries, recreation and wildlife potential because he considered the Shannon to be "one of the world's great rivers". He advised that any solution to the flood problem on the Shannon should place all related uses in their proper perspective with "the objective of benefiting all purposes insofar as is practicable" and made it specially clear from the start that he, like others in the century preceding him, had found "no simple or obvious solution".

Subsequent studies based on Rydell's work proposed an ambitious 'Summer Relief Scheme' which was thought would provide "near-immunity" to spring, summer and autumn flooding as well as a substantial reduction in the height and duration of winter floods (16). This scheme would have included the deepening of the channel between Athlone and Meelick, improving the storage capacity of Lough Ree, and the diversion of the upper Suck River into that Lough via the nearby Hind River. A diversion channel of the lower Suck River to below Meelick (suggested by Rydell as worth investigating) would have added an interesting and prominent detail across the landscape of East Galway. If this channel had been thought of last century, when time and labour seemed limitless for such projects, it might have become a reality.

The safeguarding of 'wildlife potential' was not dealt with in this Summer Relief Scheme, the details of which are elsewhere (17). With spiralling costs, the biggest question (posed in 1982) was "could £140,000,000, assuming its availability, be spent more effectively on other schemes which would be more economically, socially and environmentally acceptable?" (16)

With the entry of Environmentally Sensitive Areas (ESAs) into the arena (Chapter 7) it would seem that it can.

The floods of August-September 1985 created a new look at the Shannon by the Irish Farmer's Association. An-off-the-cuff remark that "the draining of the Shannon would compare to Ireland putting a man on the moon" points to the change of emphasis. They accepted that some flooding must always occur, but suggested that better management of water levels could alleviate a lot of hardship.

Several flooding remedies which had been suggested in the past, by professional engineers and more local commentators, were examined in a report in 1988 (21). As expected, most were non-starters and none were a comprehensive solution. The removal of the weir at Meelick, it was concluded, would only alleviate floods as far as Banagher while destroying navigation levels. The dredging of the New Cut was similarly not justifiable. Sending water down the narrow Clonahenoge Canal, in Lusmagh, would have no effect. Although this canal, the first of the original navigation works of 1755, was a massive engineering feat of its time, the amount of water it can accommodate is, of course, minuscule compared to the mighty Shannon floods. The removal (!) of Long Island just above Shannonbridge would yield no great return for the colossal effort.

Only two ideas emerged as worthy of reconsideration: localised embanking and pumping in (the few) places where a large area of callows can be protected with a short length of embankment; and the lowering of the minimum navigation level by 6" (from 7'2" to 6'8" at Banagher) regulated by the sluices in the weir at Meelick. In fact, a minimum level of 6'11" is now aimed at. Incidently, during the great 1954 flood, the gauge at Banagher read over 13'0". These sluices can modify low water-levels over the whole stretch of river to Athlone. In the crucial month of April, farming, navigation and wildlife have different requirements: the farmers want the lowest levels possible; the boat people want a reasonable water-level to prevent running aground; and the nesting wading birds require relatively high levels to use the habitat to the full. During the past few years very high rainfall and water-levels in April have made any discussion about minimum levels seem superfluous. But there have been, and will be, drier years when they assume much more importance. There were seven dry years between 1968 and 1976 when the Callows held little or no floodwater at all from the second week in March, even though the staff gauge reading reached 8'5" (= 1.08 m on the auto-gauge).

The Irish Farmer's Association, and others, called for the setting up of a Shannon Authority with statutory powers to enforce co-ordination of all aspects of the River. Instead of an Authority, a Forum was set up, which was better than nothing. Representatives of all aspects, including for the first time, wildlife conservation, meet with each other to discuss the River. Wildlife conservation on the Callows has appeared positively in submissions to the Forum from Irish Farmers' Association, Irish Wildbird Conservancy, An Taisce, Bord Failte, Office of Public Works (Wildlife Service), Offaly County Council and Teagasc (the Farm Advisory Service). So no one is now unaware.

In May 1990 the Forum met at Banagher within earshot of Corncrakes to discuss the matter of Environmentally Sensitive Areas (ESAs) and the Shannon (see Chapter 7). The question of the Authority was raised most recently in the matter of serious peat and sewage pollution of Lough Derg.

Finally, one recent viewpoint (3) ought to point the way forward. This is that drainage is increasingly unlikely to become a viable proposition for financial, ecological, and technical reasons, particularly in a Europe of over-production; that a final decision should be made to let go of unreasonable aspirations and get on with some real planning for the River and its Callows. The expertise in all aspects - farming, wildlife, navigation, water supply, pollution control - is easily found in Ireland today for political judgements to be made.

Shannon Scheme and the 'old callows'

In 1927 men walked up to ten miles each day, beating paths across bog and field to work on the Shannon Scheme between Meelick and Portumna. The Shannon Scheme, devised in 1925, started in 1927 and completed on schedule in 1929, harnessed the flow and the fall of the River below Lough Derg to produce hydro-electric power. The German firm, Siemens, was given the contract, and caused great wonder at their customs, skills and machinery, most of which had to be imported from Germany through inadequate port facilities at Limerick. The main engineering works went on south of Lough Derg and bus trips were organised from all over the country. Part of the plan was to increase the storage (and therefore the summer water-level) of Lough Derg. So, at the northern extremity of the Scheme, thirteen miles of embankment from Meelick to Portumna were raised on the Co. Galway side (see Map 2). A big workshop was erected at Keeloge (in which local dances were held), rail lines were put down to carry clay excavated from the River (and from the 2m wide drain which runs parallel) and steam-driven rollers were used to compact the clay (22).

The embankment was built to allow higher levels in summer without flooding the adjoining land. Flooding of the Callows there was actually increased for a time due to the inadvertent blocking of drains during construction, but the final result is complete year-round immunity from flooding for about 800 ha of former callowland on the Galway side of the River. MAP 3 shows that the Callows were at their widest in this section. Three pump-houses are required to keep the water from seeping up into the fields especially when the River level is higher than the fields themselves. This result is what the drainage lobby has been asking for 150 years and provides a sort of example of the possible results of 'Shannon drainage'. Whatever the official plans were, an embankment on the Tipperary side was expected locally but never materialised. Completely canalising the

EARLY CONFLICT OF INTERESTS

"Ten years ago, the late John Rennie was directed to have the Shannon surveyed to its source; not, however, as might be expected, with reference to the great object with which the consideration of that River ought to be accompanied - the improvement of its navigation - but, regarding its navigable properties of secondary importance, the survey was directed to ascertain the practability of lowering its waters, in the expectation of increasing the estates of a few proprietors, and improving the value of a few thousand acres." c. 1836 (26)

Shannon at this point would have meant impossibly high embankments and flooding downstream. Instead, the Electricity Supply Board bought affected land on the Tipperary side, and leased it back to farmers.

In its sixty years existence the embankment and its environs has created some valuable aquatic habitats and a 'model' as to what drained Callows may be like - a mosaic of intensive, 'traditional' and neglected grassland with some arable and forestry (Illus. 3.7)

In most years the Callows drain themselves by the end of May at the very latest and they become a well-used, and sometimes well-praised, agricultural resource until the end of October.

Illus. 3.7 Big-bale hay, and silage field on Friar's Island at Meelick, from the 1929 Shannon Scheme embankment by Lorraine Francis 1991.

Sixty years ago the callows on the west side of the river from Meelick to Portumna were embanked as part of the Shannon Scheme to provide hydro-electricity from the river south of Lough Derg, and flooding no longer occurs. The land is now a patchwork of grassland ranging from intensive to neglected. The field on the left of the picture has been harvested using a modern 'big-bale' harvester but retains its diverse natural flora; the field on the right has been ploughed and planted with Rye Grass for silage and intensive sheep production.

CHAPTER 4

"guaranteed freedom to produce at will"

Plant-life on the Callows

PRECIOUS STRETCH OF MEADOWLAND

"The River Shannon Callows is that precious stretch of meadowland on the river banks between Athlone and Portumna, which annually produces an extraordinary wealth of unique flora, mainly because winter flooding has restricted agricultural intensification there." 1991 (14)

The flora of the Callows is a tantalising mixture of the commonplace, the unusual and the decidely rare. The expert botanist can examine an extremely wide spectrum of plant species with relatively little effort, and still find something to make the eyebrows rise, especially in the abundant watery corners and drainage ditches. For the plant ecologist, there are plants growing together in associations which are finely tuned to habitat, their reasons for being and their strategies for survival waiting to be studied. For the lover of just flowers an arresting succession of colours is still to be seen, especially in the early season, before the grasses and sedges become the dominent feature, and later when the flowers in some of the hay meadows are in full bloom before the harvest.

Natural grassland

The Callows are semi-natural grasslands and the key part of this word is 'natural'. The grasslands of the Callows consist of a collection of native species growing on a soil which has never been ploughed or resown. Fen woodland still covered parts of the Callows as late as 1650 (1) but by 1801 most of the woodland had been cleared in Co. Offaly (then King's County) and grassland was commonplace. The Callows were then:

"richly clothed in meadow, but all insulated and, of a wet season, in a very precarious state"

and no artificial grasses had yet been introduced into the County (2). Today, the vast majority of the hay, pasture and silage fields of the countryside is the result of ploughing and reseeding at some time in the recent or more distant past.

But the Callows remain as they were. As R.L.Praeger put it as early as 1934:

"The indigenous vegetation of the lowland rich soils has been almost obliterated; the flora becomes more and more aboriginal as the soil becomes unsuitable for agricultural operations, as in bogs, marshes and mountains." (3)

But these are not quite 'natural' grasslands - to be pedantic, they are semi-natural. The human connection is clearly seen. Constant cropping, by grazing animals or by mowing machines, prevents the encroachment of willows or alders and the very gradual development (over centuries) of a sort of closed fen woodland which would probably be quite unlike the 'original' version. If agriculture ceased on the Callows the variety of plant and bird-life life described in these chapters would soon diminish.

When the natural flora and fauna of a grassland is diminished, either drastically by ploughing and reseeding, or more gradually by the heavy use of fertilizer on native grasses, the breeding bird-life is often the first to be seen to be affected. Most of the threatened bird species on a world list of the International Council for Bird Preservation (I.C.B.P.) are indeed ones which rely on large expanses of native grassland. The Corncrake is on that list. The bird-life on the Callows is still quite healthy, reflecting the relative health of the grassland.

ROBERT L. PRAEGER ON THE CALLOWS IN 1899

"Next day I worked northward along by Shannon Harbour. Arenaria tenuifolia *grew on the railway line.* Stellaria palustris, Galium uliginosum, Bidens tripartita, Carex pseudocyperus *etc grew in the swamps. My impressions of the Shannon valley were very pleasant. The great expanse of country, with the distant rim of hills - the broad slow river with its high fringe of reeds - the rich flat meadows, tinted with purple and yellow loosestrife, meadowsweet and meadow rue - the great brown bogs where curlew and plovers called incessantly." 1899 (13)*

Species list

The Callows are grasslands. Although sedges, flowers and rushes are often an equally conspicuous part of the vegetation, the Grass Family provides more species than other families of plants. The list of plant species which have been recorded within the confines of the Callows is given in Appendix 1. A great many of these are true fen species (4) because the Callows are 'man-modified' fens and marshes. They are former fens (Chapter 3) modified by the felling of original swamp woodland, modified during the navigation and drainage works of the 19th century, modified by field drains today, and modified by a certain degree of agricultural intensification, but still retaining many true fen species. The non-fen species on the Callows list are what might be called 'old dry grassland' species, an assemblage perhaps more like the "light and spiry" grasses of the drier Offaly fields in 1801 (2).

There are two hundred and sixteen plant species listed in Appendix 1. To over-simplify the rather daunting list, the species most commonly encountered when walking over the Callows fields are CUCKOO FLOWER *Cardamine pratensis* (Illus. 4.1), MARSH MARIGOLD *Caltha palustris*, WATER MINT *Mentha aquatica*, MARSH BEDSTRAW *Galium*

Illus. 4.1 Cuckoo Flower or Lady's Smock Cadamine pratensis *by Anne O'Connell 1992*

White, mauve or lilac. Flowers early, in April to June and is the commonest flower on the Callows grasslands. Perennial

Illus. 4.2 Flowering Rush Butomus umbellatus *by Anne O'Connell 1992*

Rose-pink petals with darker veins. Flowers from June to August. This is a tall, very occassional, unexpectedly handsome plant of still water in undisturbed drains and reedbeds. It is generally quite rare in Ireland and Britain.

palustre, MEADOWSWEET *Filipendula ulmaria*, WATER FORGET-ME-NOT *Myosotis scorpioides*, COMMON SEDGE *Carex nigra*, WHITE CLOVER *Trifolium repens*, MEADOW GRASS *Poa pratensis*, CREEPING BUTTERCUP *Ranunculus repens*, and CREEPING BENTGRASS *Agrostis stolonifera*. These are common and widespread species. At the other end of the spectrum, SUMMER SNOWFLAKE *Leucojum aestivum* (Illus. 4.20), BLUE-EYED GRASS *Sisyrinchium bermudiana* and FLOWERING RUSH *Butomus umbellatus* (Illus. 4.2) are very striking species of which very few individuals are found.

SUMMER SNOWFLAKE *Leucojum aestivum*
Flowers in May
Daffodil family (Amaryllidaceae)

The Summer Snowflake is unmistakeable, with a daffodil-like clump of leaves and nodding bells of creamy white, green-tipped petals. Unfortunately, although it is a plant of damp places whose seeds are carried by seasonal floods, it remains rare and exciting to find on the Callows. It is present at a handful of places mostly on the Little Brosna and in reedbeds on the Shannon downstream. One large clump was recently discovered among dense reeds at Meelick so undoubtedly others remain to be discovered.

Intriguingly, two plants have established themselves in hay meadow at Shannon Harbour around 1990, presumably from an clump which exists among reeds about half a kilometre away. On the Little Brosna river near Birr a large population of Summer Snowflake, considered native, grows under Alder woodland. The lower Shannon plants presumably are the offspring of these. Elsewhere in Ireland it is recorded from only twenty or so places spread widely across the country.

Each plant species has a 'common name' in English or Irish, and a universal 'scientific name'. The need for the latter is self-evident. Ecologists from six different European countries have their attention focused on the Callows at the moment (5). All of them speak English but are not necessarily familiar with English names for plants and birds. These English names are sometimes variable and therefore confusing. In local Callows usage 'Floating Sweet Grass' becomes 'Goose Grass", 'Meadowsweet' is 'Agrimony' and 'Snipe' (the bird) is a 'Skygoat'. A typing error in a local newspaper once produced a 'green and white-fronted grouse' instead of 'Greenland White-fronted Goose'. The scientific names can be enjoyed poetically, if nothing else.

Plant communities

"Plants are gregarious beings because they are mostly fixed in the soil, and propagate themselves in social masses." (1939) (6)

There are communities of plants on the Callows, as elsewhere. Even a brief acquaintance with the Callows at ground level (when not scanning the horizons for birds) will show that some species are more often found growing together and that some always seem to avoid each other. The dryland COCK'S FOOT GRASS *Dactylis glomerata* will never be found next to FLOATING SWEETGRASS *Glyceria fluitans*, but if the tall growing YELLOW LOOSESTRIFE *Lysimachia vulgaris* is found then REED CANARY GRASS *Phalaris arundinacea* will always be close by.

Specialists who study plant communities are called 'phyto-sociologists'. They make many lists of plant species found growing together and eventually arrive at an idea of the pattern of those which often grow together and those which rarely do so. The results are put formally into table form so the pattern can be seen at a glance. Formal names are put to the plant communities, rather like scientific names are given to the plants themselves, so that specialists from different countries can talk the same language. For the specialist, the 'phyto-sociology' of the Callows grasslands has been described elsewhere (7).

The plant communities are related to habitats, which are the result of all the environmental conditions to which plants are subject. The conditions acting on the Callows plant communities are a complex mixture of the most obvious, such as the amount of flooding they experience, especially in spring; the less visible, such as soil type; and those which need careful scientific study even to detect, such as the movement and chemistry of the water within and below the ground on which the plants are growing. Superimposed on all these are historical factors and present day management of the fields. Even old communities such as the Callows have changed and will continue to change.

The frequency and duration of flooding experienced by plants is obviously governed by their position on the Callows as regards topography. At one site 30 cm rise in river-level makes the difference between one quarter and three-quarters of a site being flooded; and governs the presence of abundant Bladder Sedge (a plant of marshes and lake-shores) in the lower grassland and Meadow Vetchling (a plant of hedges and dry grassland) in the higher.

The plant species which are there today are a product of the past. More importantly, for

nature conservation, what will be there in the future will be a product of what happens in the present.

Habitats and the plants

No-one can deny that water is a pervading feature of the Callows. Between one winter flood and the next, the Callows provide habitats for plant-life ranging from dry to permanently submerged, on a soil which ranges from peat to river alluvium. So the plant species of the Callows can usefully be described in relation to the following broad habitats, which, like in any other natural system, shade into each other and sometimes intermingle confusingly:

1. the aquatic habitat
2. wet alluvial grasslands
3. marshy grasslands
4. peatlands
5. dry grasslands

Aquatic habitats

When the spring floods finally uncover the Callows to allow the grasslands to be grazed and mown during the summer there are still places which provide habitats for plants which need to be partly or wholly submerged in water: the River's edge; the drainage ditches; and the spongy areas supplied with lime-rich spring-water. These aquatic environments have been given very little attention on the Callows and more peering into the water or, better still, a systematic survey of the whole Callows, would certainly add a significant number of species to the list in Appendix 1.

Reedbeds

As R.J. Ussher noted in 1904, there are few large expanses of Reeds on the Callows edges. Reeds grow in quiet permanent water up to a depth of about three feet, and show the winter flood level as a 'tide mark', about three feet above summer level. The Shannon Scheme in 1929 (Chapter 3), was responsible for the extensive reedbeds south of Meelick by raising the general summer level of the Shannon so that Reeds could invade the flooded field margins. A ribbon of Reeds also occurs along the river side of the embankment all the way to Portumna, on the 'dry' side, at Meelick and in other parts of the River, where quiet backwaters are slowly infilling with reedbeds and Club-rush *Scirpus lacustris*. Narrow reedbeds occur intermittently throughout the Shannon. The inner margins of reedbeds can support GREATER WATER PARSNIP *Sium latifolium*, classic climbing marshland plants such as MARSH STITCHWORT *Stellaria palustris* (Illus. 4.22), and the weak straggling plant with the potato-like flower, BITTERSWEET *Solanum dulcamara* (Illus. 4.3). At Meelick a very large and lonely individual of SUMMER SNOWFLAKE has produced its hanging bells of green-tipped flowers each spring, out of sight among the reeds, for very many years.

GREATER WATER PARSNIP *Sium latifolium*
Flowers in July to August
Carrot Family (Umbelliferae)

The Water Parsnip is a very tall, straight, imposing plant of shallow water amongst reedbeds and tall sedge communities. Of all the Callows' plants it is probably the most faithful as, in Ireland, it is found almost exclusively along the Shannon and Erne River systems. Its leaves are divided into a number of leaflets (pinnate) and each has distinctive saw-like (serrate) margins. Its white flowers, which stand at head-height exist in a wide flat-topped 'umbrella' at the end of a flowering stem which has no branches. Like many plants which live with their bases almost permanently submerged, underwater leaves are finely divided (carrot-like) and quite unlike those above the water. In most of the above description it is distinguished from the NAROW-LEAVED WATER PARSNIP which is widespread and confuses the search for its larger rarer relative. It is interesting to compare the MARSH PENNYWORT, its tiny unsuspected relative in the marshy grasslands.

Illus. 4.3 Bittersweet Solanum dulcamara by Anne O'Connell 1992

Deep purple, with a bright yellow central 'column' of anthers (similar to its close relative - the potato). Flowers in June to August. An occasional plant found most commonly on the drier edges of reedbeds and other unused tall vegetation, amongst which it climbs and twines. Perennial

MARSH STITCHWORT *Stellaria palustris*
Flowers in May to July
Pink family (Caryophyllaceae) (Illus. 4.22)

The Marsh Stitchwort is a plant often found 'straggling" among Reed Canary grass in hay meadows or among reeds themselves at the edge of reedswamp. It needs the support of these tall plants to hold its flowers high. Its flower has five white petals, but it looks like a ten-point star as each petal is almost split in two. Other stitchworts are familiar flowers of hedgerows but the stitchwort of the marsh is different. Its long, narrow leaves are a delicate bluish green, and at exactly the right time its stamens (the pollen-bearing parts on 'sticks') are ten red dots in the centre of the flower.

The distribution map shows that the Marsh Stitchwort is a plant mainly of the Shannon catchment. On the Callows it is common in suitable places.

Tall sedges

Water levels below Lusmagh/Meelick, where a lock and a weir are situated, are quite independent to those upstream. Another important Callows edge community consisting of tall sedges, was the result of the lowering of the general summer level of the Shannon by the great navigation works of the nineteenth century. An increased area of Callows margins found themselves at the borderline between permanent submergence and seasonal emergence from the flood. Tall and tussocky members of the Sedge family thrive here. Their new shoots are very close together and their energy goes upwards forming 'pedestals'

(sometimes chosen by Mallard Duck for a nest-site). The GREATER TUSSOCK SEDGE *Carex paniculata* is the commonest, and the TUFTED SEDGE *Carex elata* the rarest, most extreme example, forming tussocks up to a metre high. The widespread LESSER POND SEDGE *Carex acutiformis* and BLADDER SEDGE *Carex vesicaria* also form indifferent tussocks of a sort. At Clonmacnoise, in an area colonised by tall sedges since the navigation works of 1838, the Tufted Sedge grows in the central wettest part, looking deceptively like a smooth, luxuriant meadow, hiding its treacherous nature of unyieldingly hard tussocks set in soft mud. It is best observed through binoculars from the safety of the monastery.

Illus. 4.4 *Celery-leaved Buttercup* Ranunculus sceleratus *by Anne O'Connell 1992*

Buttercup yellow. Flowers in June to August, after which the small petals die back and a distinctive, somewhat large ovoid fruiting head is produced, unusual for Buttercups. An occasional plant of shallow water and wet mud. Annual, sometimes overwintering.

The mud, peat and silt between the pedestals is an inaccessible and little-studied habitat for plants, and provides favourite feeding for Redshank and their chicks, and Shoveler Duck. When protected from the feet of cattle looking for water, an interesting range of mud-loving species is to be found. One such plant is the uncommon CELERY-LEAVED BUTTERCUP *Ranunculus sceleratus* (Illus. 4.4).

Tall sedge areas amount to about one hundreth of the Callows area. Like its opposite community, the dry grasslands, it is a habitat small in area but high in significance.

Drainage ditches and backwaters

One of the most memorable features of the Callows is the presence of innumerable and sometimes impassable drainage ditches which impede one's progress at every turn. A mesh of drains, hundreds of kilometres long, criss-cross the Callows. There is no coordinated management to keep them cleared and functional. Consequently, there is a whole range of aquatic and semi-aquatic communities. Some have been abandoned for a long time and are merely a line of Floating Sweetgrass corresponding to a line on a 6' map. Many drains are dug down to white marl but the source of the water can be a calcareous spring from an esker or bedrock, water draining from an adjacent bog, or the Shannon level itself confined between the walls of a drain. These various aquatic environments, if studied, would be expected to show differences in the plants they support. Aquatic plant communities are very variable depending on movement of water, type of substrate and speed of silting, the chemistry of the water and the ability of the plants of recolonise after cleaning.

Aquatic plants on the Callows, as elsewhere in the world, can be conveniently divided into four types, depending on their physical relation to the water.

There are emergent plants - those which hold their leaves erect above the water

There are submerged plants - those whose leaves, and sometimes flowers, are always underwater.

There are floating/attached plants - rooted on the bottom but whose leaves float on the surface

Finally, there are a few free-floating species.

Many of these, especially the free-floating and submerged, have a close chemical relationship with the water, absorbing nutrients directly from it. Aquatic plants can therefore be used to assess the water quality (8) and some are most vulnerable to pollution.

Drains were dug mostly last century, either to drain upland fields across the Callows , to help the floods leave the Callows in spring, or to maintain a low summer water-level below the Callows fields. If there is permanent water and if they are unattended, all the above forms of aquatic plants will re-colonise the drain within a time-scale of a few weeks to a few years. Tall emergent plants which commonly choke drains with deep permanent water on the Callows are REED SWEETGRASS *Glyceria maxima*, BRANCHED BUR-REED *Sparganium erectum*, and the COMMON REED *Phragmites australis*. A very effective and common choking species is NARROW-LEAVED WATER PARSNIP *Berula erecta* which spreads a mesh of underwater stems. In more shallow summer water BOGBEAN *Menyanthes trifoliata*, MARSH HORSETAIL *Equisetum palustre* and, where the water is particularly calcareous, WATERCRESS *Nasturtium* spp. and FOOL'S WATERCRESS *Apium nodiflorum* have the same effect, and the BOTTLE SEDGE *Carex rostrata* is common.

Smaller plant species, such as LEAST BUR-REED *Sparganium minimum* and LESSER WATER-PLANTAIN *Baldellia ranunculoides*, emerge sparsely to hold their very different flowers above the water. The tree-like branching of the large FINE-LEAVED WATER DROPWORT *Oenanthe aquatica*, at first dark and submerged and later emerging bright green with small clusters of white flowers, invites comparison with the oak. The COMMON DUCKWEED *Lemna minor* is a ubiquitous free-floating species, thousands of whose tiny bright green leaves not only cover the surface of a drain but also are carried amongst the flotsam of dead reed stems to live briefly high up on the Callows floodline. Another duckweed whose individual consists of just one translucent leaf and one root is IVY-LEAVED DUCKWEED *Lemna trisulca* and always free-floats just beneath the surface. A third species is the FAT DUCKWEED *Lemna gibba* (Illus. 4.5) which has a strangely inflated underside to the leaf and can also be abundant.

Much sparser is GREATER DUCKWEED *Spirodella polyrhiza* with a 'tassel' of roots beneath its larger single circular leaves.

The Common Duckweed is not only ubiquitous on the Callows but cosmopolitan throughtout the world in both hemispheres except for Polar regions and the deep Tropics - a truly successful species.

FROGBIT *Hydrocharis morsus-ranae*
Flowers in July and August
Frogbit Family (Hydrocharitaceae)

The Frogbit is the largest of the free-floating plants. It produces white, delicate, short-lived, three-petalled flowers, with an arresting yellow 'eye', from among groups of floating dark green, kidney-shaped leaves and a tassle of roots. When held against the light the leaves have a very beautiful network pattern of veins. It borrows a spreading stategy from land-based plants (or is it vice versa ?) in having 'stolons', stems which grow out horizontally from the plant to produce more roots, leaves, flowers and more stolons. In this way it can quickly cover the water surface to produce a display of flowers in late summer. With these stolons, this truly aquatic plant species can creep out of the water if overcrowding of leaves takes place or an unusually dry spell restricts the water surface.

Ice in winter would kill these free-floating plants if buds (called 'turions') did not sink to the bottom to rest among the mud, silt or reed debris, to sprout and rise again to the surface in early summer. Other Callows aquatics produce 'turions' in this way - Whorled Water Milfoil and the Lesser Pondweed, to name two.

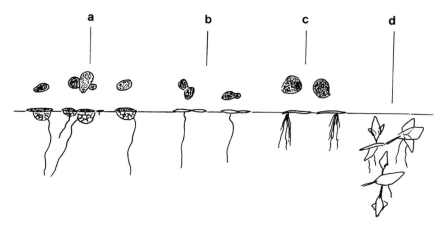

Illus. 4.5 The Duckweeds

a) Fat Duckweed,
b) Common Duckweed,
c) Greater Duckweed,
d) Ivy-leaved Duckweed.

The YELLOW WATER LILY *Nuphar lutea* and the larger WHITE WATER-LILY *Nymphaea alba* grow in deep water, beyond the reeds, in places along the Callows edge and in backwaters. Their leaves are not free-floating but permanently attached to runners in the bottom sediments. The elegant ARROWHEAD *Sagittaria sagittifolia* belongs in deep water also. Its submerged and floating leaves are straplike but the striking arrowhead leaves are held clear of the water. The large yellow buttercup GREATER SPEARWORT *Ranunculus lingua* (Illus. 4.8) is by no means common but grows tall and straight out of permanent water.

Other floating/attached species include the grasses and grass-like species whose leaves float limply on the surface of the water. FLOATING SWEETGRASS *Glyceria fluitans* is common and provides an ecological link with the wet alluvial grassland described below. AMPHIBIOUS BISTORT *Polygonum amphibium*

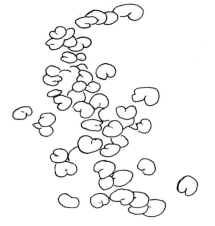

Illus. 4.6..Frogbit leaves on the surface of a drain

Illus. 4.7 Broad-leaved Pondweed on the surface of a drain

has two distict forms - an almost hairless, aquatic form with flat floating leaves, and a roughly hairy upright form which can become abundant in wet alluvial grassland. WATER WHORL GRASS *Catabrosa aquatica* is local, in areas with particularly calcareous groundwater. Its almost iridescent green leaves can be mistaken for the common Floating Sweetgrass, but it produces an unmistakeable panicle of hazy blue spikelets (flowers). Long floating leaves of the UNBRANCHED BUR-REED or STRAPWEED *Sparganium emersum* are present in the 'canal' by the embankment at Meelick, and elsewhere.

Pondweeds are typical plants of the still, permanent water of drains. Their mundane sounding name is deceptive, they are a difficult and interesting group of aquatic plants. Of the floating pondweeds, the BROAD-LEAVED PONDWEED *Potamogeton natans* (Illus. 4.7) is widespread, while the FEN PONDWEED *Potamogeton coloratus* is present in a shallow ditch fed by particularly calcareous springwater from beneath the esker bounding the north side of the Little Brosna, and similar situations elsewhere. The submerged, sparse, grass-like LESSER PONDWEED *Potamogeton pusillus* grows in deeper water where the waters of the Shannon extend four miles up the Little Brosna along the Main Drain. Here also the rare RIVER WATER DROPWORT *Oenanthe fluviatilis* has a tenuous hold. The water milfoils have the capacity to grow in abundance beneath the surface of the water. The SPIKED WATER MILFOIL *Myriophyllum spicatum* is probably widespread, and the WHORLED WATER MILFOIL *Myriophyllum verticillatum*

produces an underwater 'forest' in the Little Brosna ditch, but hold its flower spikes above the surface. Their beauty is sometimes marred by the greeny brown BLANKETWEED (algae) adhering to the feathery leaves as they reach

Illus. 4. 8 Greater Spearwort Ranunculus lingua by Anne O'Connell 1992

Buttercup yellow. Flowers in June and July. A large-flowered, occasional plant of permanent water in drains and reedbeds. In Ireland it is most frequent in the Shannon catchment. The LESSER SPEARWORT (Ranunculus flammula) is less than half its size, otherwise very similar and is common on the callows grasslands. Perennial

the surface. Despite its appearance Blanketweed is most important to the ecology of these places, providing abundant food and refuge for aquatic animals such as snails.

OPPOSITE-LEAVED PONDWEED
Groenlandia densa
Pondweed family (Potamogetonaceae)

The Opposite-leaved Pondweed is on the Irish Flora Protection Order as it has only been recorded from a handful of places recently. Among pondweeds it has an unmistakeable feathery appearance on account of its geometrically opposite leaves.

Its former distribution on the Shannon is not known but it likes clear water and is declining, in Ireland and throughout its range across Europe due to pollution and silting of its habitat. It has been found recently at Meelick in the 'canal' alongside of the embankment away from the River. It grows in clear water, away from the controversy of sewage pollution and peat siltation on the River itself. It is a habitat created only sixty years ago by the Shannon Scheme and the 'canal' has been lightly cleared annually, often with a 'scythe on a long pole'. Fears that too much physical disturbance of the 'canal' might destabilize the embankment may mean a continuation of this light clearing, which in turn should help this precariously small population to survive here.

Other Pondweeds are waiting to be found in the waters of the Callows and their river margins. Five extra are present in the River Suck south of Ballinasloe and can be expected to have made their way down to the Shannon: Shining Pondweed *Potamogeton lucens*, Various-leaved Pondweed *P. gramineus*, Curled Pondweed *P. crispus*, Perfoliate Pondweed *P. perfoliatus*, and Small Pondweed *P. berchtoldii* (J. Caffrey)

It is tempting to dwell too much here on the fascinating world of underwater plants on the Callows, the beauty of whose waving, water-supported forms is different and more easily appreciated than the often crowded communities of terrestrial plants. Drains with permanent deep water are not abundant and are scattered along the Callows. The most easily accessible is the ten-mile Shannon Scheme 'canal' from Meelick to below the bridge at Portumna and the E.S.B. main drain which dissects the callows on the north side of the Little Brosna.

Calcareous springs

The unseen water under the surface of the ground is called 'groundwater'. The hybrid phrase 'eco-hydrology' is the study of the relationship between wild plant species (as opposed to agricultural crop species) and groundwater movement and chemistry. Research in the Netherlands, where water quality for both human use and nature conservation is taken very seriously, has shown the relationship to be, not surprisingly, rather complicated but vitally important (9). The eco-hydrology of the mid-Shannon region, centering very much of the Callows, is the subject of an intensive study at the time of writing (1991-94) and the results should reveal fascinating insights into the Callows plant communities (5). WATERCRESS *Nasturtium* sp (Illus. 4.9) has long been seen by drainage engineers in Ireland as an indicator of land which is undrainable because of a permanently seeping groundwater.

At a number of places along the Callows groundwater emerges in the form of springs or seepage and the effect on the plant species composition is highly visible. The occurrence of these fascinating places have yet to be mapped and some are only temporary, existing for a few weeks after the spring floods have receded and before the winter floods appear. Only one, a permanently green half-acre amid the annual colour change of the Callows between Banagher and Shannon Harbour, has been looked at. WATERCRESS and FOOL'S WATERCRESS *Apium nodiflorum* grow in luxurious abundance (hiding Water Rail) along with WATER WHORL GRASS *Catabrosa aquatica*, FLOATING SWEETGRASS *Glyceria fluitans*, PLICATE SWEETGRASS *Glyceria plicata*, a hybrid between the last two, with no common name, called Glyceria x pedicellata. GYPSYWORT *Lycopus europaeus* and HEMP-AGRIMONY *Eupatorium cannabinum* are tall herbs here. LONG-STALKED YELLOW SEDGE *Carex lepidocarpa* and BLUNT-FLOWERED RUSH *Juncus subnodulosus* have stems covered in calcareous tufa and the STONEWORT *Chara vulgaris*, brittle with tufa, exists here also.

GRASSLANDS on the Callows

It is, of course, impossible to describe every square metre of the Callows grasslands. However, terrestrial communities are much more stable than aquatic ones. Those described here are typical, and are more or less repeated with variations, throughout the Callows.

Wet alluvial grassland

(Floating Sweetgrass community)

Sometimes the waters of the Little Brosna come down from the Slieve Bloom, under the final stone bridge at Newbridge, with a heavy load of alluvium. This is spread out over the callows through breaks in the man-made banks built to carry the river at a level above the callows when the Shannon is not in flood. The rich luxuriance of this community of plants bears witness to the fertilizing effect of the silt-laden floods - a phenomenon which is as yet unquantified but probably not widespread on the Callows as a whole.

The soft, long-leaved FLOATING SWEETGRASS *Glyceria fluitans* is not only "eagerly taken by cattle" but is also eagerly taken by grazing duck such as Wigeon. It is dominant (along with CREEPING BENT GRASS) in grassland which is often still under floodwater at the beginning of the growing season in March/April. If the fields are not grazed heavily during the summer, the the dark green COMMON SPIKE-RUSH *Eleocharis palustris* joins the grass, and its millet-like seeds form an abundant source of food for the yearly

Illus. 4.9 Watercress Nasturtium officinale by Anne O'Connell 1992

White. Flowers in June to August. A plant of shallow drains and other wet places, especially where these are fed by particularly lime-rich water. Unrelated to the garden "Nasturtiums'. Perennial

influx of wildfowl. In heavily grazed fields the CURLED DOCK *Rumex crispus* becomes abundant, also food for wildfowl. The WATER DOCK *Rumex hydrolapathum*, an impressive and uncommon species, resembles a giant aberration of a Curled Dock with leaves a metre in height and the flowers even higher. It is a scarce plant of reedswamp and drains, but a single ungrazed individual found in the midst of wet alluvial grassland on the Little Brosna callows hints at the transitional nature between aquatic habitats and wet alluvial grassland on the Callows. These fields can be very wet in summer. The presence of DUCKWEED *Lemna minor* and MARE'S TAIL *Hippuris vulgaris* amongst the grass in parts of the Little Brosna gives a similar hint.

The phenomenon of wetland plants in ordinary fields is put well in *'The Natural History of the Somerset Levels'* (10) "Many of the plants of the ditches seem to spill out into the fields - or so it seems; in fact the opposite is true". In agriculturally improved fields on the Levels these plants survive only on the edges of drains. In 'unimproved fields' they take their rightful place across the whole field. Among many such flowers on the Callows, mostly 'unimproved fields', are: the four-petalled YELLOW CRESSES , especially GREATER YELLOW CRESS *Rorippa amphibia* but also MARSH YELLOW CRESS *R. palustris* and, more rarely, CREEPING YELLOW CRESS *R. sylvestris*; the common, five-petalled WATER FORGET-ME-NOT *Myosotis scorpioides*, blue with a yellow 'eye'; and of course, most characteristically, MARSH MARIGOLD *Caltha palustris*. The wetland SPEEDWELLS *Veronica* spp) belong in this category, the small flowers of each species having a distinctive shade of blue or pink: MARSH SPEEDWELL *Veronica scutellata* - white or pale blue; BLUE WATER SPEEDWELL *Veronica anagallis-aquatica* - pale blue; PINK WATER SPEEDWELL *Veronica catenata* - pink; and BROOKLIME *Veronica beccabunga* - a deep and striking blue.

Brooklime is found on wet mud and can be accompanied by the WATER CROWFOOT *Ranunculus aquatilis* (Illus. 4.10), an ambivalent species, normally found in shallow permanent water where it covers the surface with its white, buttercup-like flowers. Underwater leaves are intricately and finely divided, while the leaves which float are circular, only slightly toothed. Its seeds are easily spread and the late-receding floods of May 1992 showed its ambivalent nature well. Its flowers abundantly occupied the water remaining in a tractor-made depression far from any drain. As the

Illus. 4.10 Common Water Crowfoot Ranunculus aquatilis *by Anne O'Connell 1992*

White, with a yellow 'eye'. Flowers in May to August. A plant of permanent shallow water, or temporary annual springs and pools. As an annual it sets seeds as the pool dries, to germinate again the next Spring as the pool emerges from the falling flood. The divided leaves are produced underwater while the wedge-shaped leaves are floating or are produced as the water dries up. Annual or perennial

water dried out, its underwater leaves withered to be replaced by its round aerial leaves, it set seed, disappeared and will sprout again there only if the floods are late again.

The Floating Sweetgrass community covers over one quarter of the Little Brosna callows but elsewhere on the Callows is sparse and rarely extends over more than a few hectares at a time.

Marshy grasslands

(Creeping Buttercup-Common Sedge community)

In the modern parlance of plant ecology the technical and perhaps evocative term 'mire' is used to embrace all wetlands which consist of sedges, grasses, rushes and flowers growing on peat. Traditionally, 'fen' grows on base-rich peat, 'bog' grows on acid peat, and 'marsh' grows on a soil which is not peat. The grasslands described in this section grow on "peaty, silty, clay loam" and so the aide-memoire 'marshy grasslands' seems appropriate.

MARSH MARIGOLD *Caltha palustris*
Flowers in March to June
Buttercup family (Ranunculaceae)

The Marsh Marigold commonly creates dots, splashes or carpets of yellow on the marshy grasslands throughout the Callows as early as April (not to be confused with the yellow of dandelions on the drier Callows at the same time). Its heart-shaped leaves and large bright yellow flowers are so familiar that they could almost be an emblem of the Callows. But the conspicuous flower has no petals. The yellow beacon which attracts pollinating insects are sepals (normally a ring of green, leaf-like parts behind the petals). It is thought that this lack of petals makes the flower one of the most 'primitive' in the Irish flora, perhaps a form of flower unchanged for millions of years.

A plant of streamsides in the wild and in the garden, the Marsh Marigold is particularly suited to the seasonal flooding, and lime-rich alluvium of the Callows. It thrives even more in partly shaded places and can be imagined within the swamp woodlands of the past.

The bulk of these grasslands, especially the pastures, is made up of two quite different interwoven species - CREEPING BENT GRASS *Agrostis stolonifera* and COMMON SEDGE *Carex nigra*. The grass has long, leafy overground stems which root and form a loose mat; the sedge has underground stems from which arise many dense tufts. Both can dominate the Callows vegetation, often together.

BROWN SEDGE *Carex disticha*
Flowers in May and June
Sedge Family (Cyperaceae)

Brown Sedge spreads itself more sparsely than the Common Sedge due to an orderly arrangement of single or double shoots arising from very far-reaching underground stems (or rhizomes). The bright green leaves are noticeable amongst the rather dull more abundant Common Sedge. The flowerhead is a dense brown uniform cluster of spikelets. The only sedge on the Callows with flowers like these is the Greater Tussock Sedge, and its 'pedestal' form could not be more unlike the Brown Sedge.

Several other grasses are scattered around the marshy grassland habitat, sometimes abundantly. There are two contrasting grasses whose habitats converge on the Callows. MEADOW FESCUE *Festuca pratensis* - "a valuable grazing and hay grass for rich moist soils" (11) - has wide, soft, bright green leaves and panicles of nodding greenish or bluish spikelets (flowers). Conversely, TUFTED HAIR GRASS *Deschampsia cespitosa* - "a coarse worthless grass of wet and badly drained soils" - has narrow, stiff, dark green leaves which cut the fingers if rubbed downwards. The showy panicle is, however, ornamental, with spikelets of shining green, gold, silver and purple. Ignored by cattle, except sometimes to pull up and discard, this grass can form large wide tussocks. ROUGH MEADOW GRASS *Poa trivialis* and SMOOTH MEADOW GRASS *Poa pratensis* are widespread on the Callows and the imposing TALL FESCUE *Festuca arundinacea* less so.

MARSH BEDSTRAW *Galium palustre*
Flowers in June to August
Bedstraw family (Rubiaceae)

The Marsh Bedstraw is a commonplace plant of the Callows. The flowers are small, with four white petals. Despite their size the flowers are abundant on the plant and can make a good contribution to the detail of colour on the Callows. Like many Callows flowers it 'leans' on taller plants to grow well and in these situations it seems to be mostly stem and flowers. The leaves are in 'whorls' (like the spokes of a wheel) of four or five at the points where each head of flowers divides from the stem. The FEN BEDSTRAW *Galium uliginosum* is very similar but its leaves are six or eight in a whorl with a distinct point (mucronate). It is a plant of the Callows peatlands and not at all common.

The ability of a plant to grow quickly along the ground (creeping) and take root, though still joined some distance away from the parent, is a common one in lands liable to flood. It allows plants to spread quickly into bare spaces caused by the spreading of alluvium or heavy grazing of soft ground. CREEPING BUTTERCUP and CREEPING BENTGRASS are abundant and others without the 'creeping' epithet are also characteristic of these 'flood swards' - SILVERWEED *Potentilla anserina* , FLOATING SWEETGRASS, MARSH FOXTAIL *Alopecurus geniculatus*, WATER SPEEDWELL *Veronica anagallis-aquatica*, BROOKLIME *Veronica beccabunga*. CREEPING JENNY *Lysimachia nummularia*, whose vivid yellow flowers are bigger than its heart-shaped leaves, is a striking and uncommon plant creeping (but not rooting) deep among the grasses or forming carpets on bare ground.

YELLOW LOOSESTRIFE *Lysimachia vulgaris*
Flowers in July
Primrose family (Primulaceae)

The Yellow Loosestrife is a close relative of the Creeping Jenny and its flowers are a similar yellow, large and striking. But it could not be more different in form. It is tall and upright, and holds its flowers in a showy arrangement of twenty or more in a cluster set off by the green of a few leaves. It is a flower of hay meadows, invariably a companion of Reed Canary Grass, and coming into its own if the meadows are cut even later than usual.

In the hay meadows plant species (as well as Corncrakes) can grow undisturbed until the beginning of July at least.

REED CANARY GRASS *Phalaris arundinacea*
Flowers in June and July
Grass family (Gramineae)

The Reed Canary grass is the tall, reed-like grass, with stiff green-blue leaves of every hay meadow in the marshy grasslands, sometimes in widely extensive and dense stands. Late June in these places produces a sea of purple, the colour of its spikelets (small grass flowers). In a wet year when the hay remains uncut, this turns to a straw brown sea.

Although the seeds are perhaps too small and the winter leaves too tough to contribute much to wildfowl food, the Reed Canary Grass is a useful plant on the Callows. Uncut leaves overwinter and begin to grow early and fast, providing early cover for Corncrake - by mid-June it can be more than waist-high. It is highly productive, and can absorb pollutants into its roots without affecting the leaves.

In certain instances of high alluvial fertility there can be a striking large-scale pattern of green-blue Canary Grass with dark green Spike-Rush. (Illus. 4.21).

Almost all the plant species of the Callows grasslands can be found within the hay meadows, and usually to their best advantage, growing through all stages of maturity before the harvest. Some, however, are confined to this habitat which allows tall growing herbs to set seed before the annual "sacrifice to the mower's blade". These tall herbs often grow even better in uncut corners of fields reminding us of their origins in clearings in the ancient fen woodland. The specific scientific name of WILD ANGELICA *Angelica sylvestris* means after all 'of woodland' and WILD VALERIAN *Valeriana officinalis*, delicate pink clusters of small flowers, is a tall herb of damp woodland. Its seeds have suprisingly, if minutely, ornate feathery attachments. MEADOW RUE *Thalictrum flavum*, with its haze of petal-less fragrant, creamy-yellow flowers, still grows in hay meadows north of Banagher (and elsewhere) where Praeger noted it almost a hundred years ago. SNEEZEWORT *Achillea ptarmica* looks like an all-white Daisy, an unusually large cluster can have a brilliance never quite captured in flower book illustrations.

MARSH PEA *Lathyrus palustris*
Flowers in June and July
Pea Family (Leguminosae) (Illus. 4.12)

The Marsh Pea is a flower of ungrazed places on the Callows, often within Canary Grass or reeds and often in hay meadows. In 1954 Praeger described it as being encountered "here and there" on the Callows, and so it remains. It is known from eighteen small patches along the River, and in great and famous abundance at Clonmacnoise.

The flowers of Marsh Pea are quite large - deep

magenta with the typical peaflower arrangement of five petals, described in the Floras as "a standard, two wings and a keel made up of two lower petals". Its long leaves appear in early June and with the help of twisting tendrils it climbs up with the growing grass and holds its flowers and black pods at a height.

The Marsh Pea is a little understood plant. It was recently taken off the the list of Irish protected plants (Flora Protection Order) because it was not quite rare enough (it remains protected in Northern Ireland). It is reported as becoming a weed when established in the garden, yet in the wild it will grow among reeds which are submerged for half the year. It seems to benefit from drier conditions and at Clonmacnoise it appeared to thrive with increased fertilisation.

Some 90% of the Callows can be classed as 'marshy grasslands' occurring between the very low-lying wet grasslands and the peatlands / dry grasslands.

MARSH PENNYWORT *Hydrocotyle vulgaris*
Flowers in May to July
Carrot family (Umbelliferae)

The Marsh Pennywort is a common species, seen as shiny circular creeping leaves about 3 cm in diameter, lying close to the ground amongst the grasses and sedges. Its flowers are a delicate pinkish-green, if only they were noticed. They are tiny and held even closer to the ground than the leaves. A magnifying glass brings out their beauty.

The Callows Peatlands

(Carnation Sedge-Red Fescue or 'small-sedge' community)

The Shannon is not a turbulent river and the quiet floodwaters that spread towards the edges of the Callows carry no alluvium. Consequently, the plants here grow on peat soils which are relics of the quieter period's fen development (Chapter 2). On the best examples, more plants grow together in these communities than in others on the Callows - it is 'species-rich' because no tall, fast growing competitive plants exist on the impoverished peat soils and yet many species thrive in the freedom from severe spring flooding.

The SEDGE FAMILY of plants (Cyperaceae) is quite rightly associated in people's minds with wet places and the sedges of the Callows provide a list of plant species second only in length to the Grass Family. Whether flowering or not (they are often among the first plants of the Callows to do so) sedges are easily distinguished from grasses. In most Callows sedge species the male flowers (bearing pollen) and female flowers (producing seeds) are on quite separate 'spikes', unique to each type of sedge. In a few types, the male and female flowers are intermixed. Compare, for instance, the Carnation, Glaucous and Brown Sedges. In the absence of flowers, sedges are distinguished from grasses by triogonal (three-sided) features, especially the stem.

The term 'sedge-rich grasslands' is an apparently contradictory term which aptly describes the species composition of the peatlands on the Callows. Low growing sedges dominate a rich variety of other species. These sedges are quite different from the tall, long-leaved, robust pedestals of sedges of the River's edge (see 'Tall Sedges' above). The YELLOW SEDGE *Carex flava* agg. and CARNATION SEDGE *Carex panicea* usually dominate the sward accompanied by the wiry leaves of the FLEA SEDGE *Carex pulicaris* and the sedge-like BRISTLE CLUB-RUSH *Scirpus setaceus*. The GLAUCOUS SEDGE *Carex flacca* and sometimes, SPRING-SEDGE *Carex caryophyllea* appear on the drier end of the peatland sites, and the TAWNY SEDGE *Carex hostiana* can dominate the wetter hollows. Tawny is exactly the colour of these places in autumn before the leaves die off for winter.

The YELLOW SEDGE community occurs on flat land where the peat is fed by mineral-rich groundwater, next to eskers or hills. On the other hand, the STAR SEDGE *Carex echinata* replaces the YELLOW SEDGE where the peat, not fed by such water, is half-way to becoming a bog, or where the bogs run down to the Callows. FEN BEDSTRAW *Galium uliginosum*, RAGGED-ROBIN *Lychnis flos-cuculi*, and COMMON COTTON GRASS *Eriophorum angustifolium* are found with the STAR SEDGE. At Clonmacnoise other sedges are added to the list in this special type of 'sedge rich grassland'

Illus. 4.11 Butterfly Orchid

Creamy white Orchid found in places where the Callows are very peaty, almost a Bog. (Photo: S. Heery)

Illus. 4.12 Marsh Pea
(Photo: S. Heery)

- SLENDER SEDGE *Carex lasiocarpa*, LESSER TUSSOCK SEDGE *Carex diandra*, OVAL SEDGE *Carex ovalis*, DIOECIOUS SEDGE *Carex dioica* - reflecting the complex nature of these bog-cum-callow peats. The BUTTERFLY ORCHID *Platanthera* sp.) is a large winged creamy white orchid of these places (Illus. 4.11).

MARSH CINQUEFOIL *Potentilla palustris*
Flowers June and July
Rose Family (Rosaceae)

The flower of Marsh Cinquefoil is quite unlike the other Potentillas of the Callows (Tormentil and Silverweed) which have 'conventional' yellow flowers. The purple star consists of five sepals behind its small, red petals. It is a plant

Illus. 4.13 Bog or Meadow Thistle Cirsium dissectum *by Anne O'Connell 1992*

Deep purple. Flowers in June to August. A common plant mainly in peaty Callows grasslands. If ungrazed it can become colourfully abundant. The prickles on the leaves are harmlessly soft. Perennial.

of wet, peaty, lime-free places and so is an abundant companion to the Star Sedge where the Callows are adjacent to bogs, and in overgrown drains which do not reach the lime-rich white marl. Its leaves are somewhat 'strawberry-like' and its tough runners can spread a mat over very wet ground or even water.

Grasses take a subservient place in these sedge-rich grasslands. The unobtrusive HEATH GRASS *Danthonia decumbens* and the commoner RED FESCUE *Festuca rubra* seem most at home here while the showy flowers of QUAKING GRASS *Briza media* are beautifully conspicuous in the hay meadows or lesser grazed fields. Grasses of the drier more fertile grasslands such as the soft and downy YORKSHIRE FOG GRASS *Holcus lanatus*, CRESTED DOG'S TAIL *Cynosurus cristatus* and SWEET VERNAL GRASS *Anthoxanthum odoratum* are small and weak unless fertilised. The purple MEADOW or BOG THISTLE *Cirsium dissectum* (Illus. 4.13) is common. GRASS OF PARNASSUS *Parnassia palustris* has an eye-catching single flower, the white petals have dark veins strangely reminiscent of the Green-veined White butterfly which is abundant over the Callows meadows. It can be in flower as late as October.

BOG PIMPERNELL *Anagallis tenella*
Flowers in July and August
Primrose family (Primulaceae)

The Bog Pimpernel can be found amongst the low sedges on the peatiest ground. It has somewhat large delicate pink funnel-shaped flowers, although its leaves are tiny on thin stems that creep tenaciously along the ground.

PURGING or FAIRY FLAX *Linum catharticum*, a diminutive relative of the cultivated flax whose stems are used to make linen thread (and seeds to make linseed oil), is a tiny white-flowered, straggling plant typical of these places, as well as the dry grasslands

The dry grasslands
(Meadow Vetchling-Red Fescue community)

Dry grassland occurs on old river alluvium or glacial material which just about rises above most of the flooding. The term dry grassland may seem out of place in a description of the Callows where flooding is seen to be the most pervasive feature, and indeed only about one hundredth of the Callows are such. Wet grassland was described as often being flooded in springtime when plant-life begins to grow. Dry grassland occurs only one metre above this level and is rarely flooded in spring (or even winter). Furthermore, at this height, and with these soils, water drains freely from the surface and rooting zone of the plants. So there exists a community of plants more suited to the dry 'upland' than to the Callows. They owe their survival to their 'insignificant' area and to their being surrounded by wet callowland in spring.

In the Callows wetlands we have examples of plant communities which were once common and are becoming rare. In the dry grasslands we have examples of plant communities which were once ubiquitous but are now even rarer.

The two-inch high, single-leafed fern ADDER'S TONGUE *Ophioglossum vulgatum* (Illus. 4.14) can be extraordinarily abundant at ground level if the grasses are parted. The pink COMMON SPOTTED ORCHID *Dactylorhiza*

Illus. 4.14 Adder's Tongue Fern Ophioglossum vulgatum *by Anne O'Connell 1992*

Green. This is a very small Fern, barely 5 cm high, of the infrequently flooded, dry grassland 'rises' on the Callows. In this situation it can be suprisingly abundant, if inconspicuous, amongst the grass. Spores to be carried on the wind are produced on the cobra-like spike which is actually part of the leaf and can be present from May to August. It also spreads itself by underground stems.

Illus. 4.17 Hay Rattle Rhinanthus minor by Anne O'Connell 1992

Yellow. Flowers in May to July. An abundant plant of dry alluvial grasslands on the Callows. The ripe seeds are contained in the inflated 'calyx' behind the petals, and thus will rattle if shaken. The plant is annual and semi-parasitic on the roots of some of its companion plants. A closely related plant, the RED RATTLE (Pedicularis palustris) also annual, occurs in an opposing habitat - wet peaty grassland.

Illus. 4.16 Eyebright Euphrasia sp. by Anne O'Connell 1992

White, mauve or lilac with a yellow 'eye'. Flowers July and August. An occasional, only locally abundant, plant of dry grasslands on the Callows. Annual and semi-parasitic. To recognise the myriad varieties and fertile hybrids of Eyebrights in Ireland is a task for expert botanists.

fuchsii begins to flower in June, as does the unobtrusive, green TWAYBLADE ORCHID *Listera ovata*. The COWSLIP *Primula veris*, more familiar in 'upland' pasture and a protected plant in Northern Ireland, flowers and sets seed in April and May in the open grassland before the hay meadow grows up to obscure the low rossettes of leaves. The list of flowers

Illus. 4.15 Bird's Foot Trefoil Lotus corniculatus by Anne O'Connell 1992

Bright yellow with a hint of blood-red in the bud. Flowers in June to September. One of the commonest wayside flowers in Ireland, and on the Callows it is abundant in the dry grasslands. Its less common, slightly larger but very similar relative, GREATER BIRD'S FOOT TREFOIL (Lotus uliginosus), could probably be found in damper places on the Callows, and can be distinguished by the presence of long sparse hairs.

amongst the grasses, long but not endless, provides dots and splashes of colour (Illus. 4.18). The PEA family contributes the yellow MEADOW VETCHLING *Lathyrus pratensis*, BIRD'S FOOT TREFOIL *Lotus corniculatus* (Illus. 4.15), and BLACK MEDICK *Medicago lupulina*; the blue-violet TUFTED VETCH *Vicia cracca* (Illus. 4.19); and the RED CLOVER *Trifolium pratense*. The large OX-EYE DAISY *Leucanthemum vulgare* and HAWKSBEARDS *Crepis species*, with dandelion-like flowers on branched stems, grow conspicuously tall

following the growth of the grasses. Small but robust EYEBRIGHT *Euphrasia* sp. (Illus. 4.16), partly parasitic on the roots of other plants, can be found where thinner soils discourage competition with the tall grasses. The similarly parasitic YELLOW RATTLE *Rhinanthus minor* (Illus. 4.17) is more widespread.

In contrast to the rest of the Callows, grass species are found here in their richest variety. If the common roadside grass COCK'S FOOT *Dactylis glomerata* is present then it is dry

Illus. 4.18 Species-rich colour
(Photo: S. Heery)

The Common Spotted Orchid (pink), Bird's Foot Trefoil (yellow) , Tufted Vetch (purple) and Meadowsweet (cream) providing colour in a species - rich dry grassland community on the Callows.

grassland. The OAT-GRASSES are particularly associated with dry grassland and they each have an oat-like awn (a bristle-like point) on each flower. The tall and leafy FALSE OAT-GRASS *Arrhenatherum elatius* has silvery shining flowers and a deep roots which make it resistant to drought. The YELLOW OAT-GRASS *Trisetum flavescens* is much lower growing, with golden green shining flowers.

Even in 1954, during the post-war drive to improve grassland and increase arable land in Britain, the significance of pockets of natural and semi-natural places for the survival of 'special associations of grasses' was recognised (11). And that was forty years ago. Since then the pockets have become even smaller. Grass has been the mainstay of animal husbandry, and today there is a dependence on one species, Rye Grass, with many artificially-created variations. Grasses, even the original native variety of Rye Grass, which used to feed the animals, are left to survive as 'weeds' or in these 'special associations'. What happens if there is suddenly a Rye Grass disease ? A frantic search would go on for substitutions.

Where five or six grasses grow together, their leaves, stems and root systems inextricably mixed in close association in the same postage stamp area of grassland (say four square metres), the impact of agricultural intensification is thought to be minimal and hence the conservation value maximal. Ten grasses co-exist on the best examples of these dry grasslands on the Callows. Along with the FALSE OAT-GRASS and YELLOW OAT-GRASS, most of the following occur: SWEET VERNAL GRASS, YORKSHIRE FOG, TIMOTHY GRASS, RYE GRASS, RED FESCUE, MEADOW FESCUE, TALL FESCUE, SMOOTH MEADOW GRASS, ROUGH MEADOW GRASS, QUAKING GRASS, CRESTED DOG'S TAIL, MEADOW BROME GRASS and COCK'S FOOT. There is one sedge, set apart from its wetland relatives, which grows among these grasses - the aptly named HAIRY SEDGE *Carex hirta*.

MEADOW BROME *Bromus commutatus*, an annual grass with a few fat spikelets of awned flowers, rather rare in Ireland and scattered on the Callows, sets next year's seed before the harvest. There is a distinct possibility of other rare grasses surviving in the Callows dryland communities.

Oat Grass meadows are considered to be the natural grassland which replaced the original woodland all over Europe from east to west on soils which are neither too wet nor too dry. These are the perfect soils for agricultural improvement so, of course, survivors are rare. This old mixture of grasses usually occurs at the high end of a long strip of hay meadow and soon grades into more normal callowland. Irish Oat Grass meadows are different from their European counterparts on account of the extreme oceanic climate (mild, damp and cloudy). The best examples may survive in neglected graveyards and roadside verges. The Callows Oat Grass meadows are at the extreme end of dampness, sometimes even flooded. The gradation from dry grassland to wetland at one site is so short that shoots of REEDS grow up through the OAT GRASS, an unusual association of species to be sure !

The soils under these dry grasslands have not yet been studied but the communities

Illus. 4.19 Dragonfly on Tufted Vetch by Anne O'Connell 1992

This dragonfly has chosen the right flower on which to rest from its predatory flights. The purple TUFTED VETCH, a common Callows flower, has over thirty insect species associated with it. Uncut, rank areas on the edges of the Callows drains and backwaters, or on upland bogs and hedgerows are important breeding sites for insects which then move into the flower-rich meadows as the summer progresses. Flooding and mowing are traumatic annual events for the insect population.

described above probably occur on river alluvium, either naturally occurring or the result of nineteenth century navigation works. The botanical interest of a plant community is not proportional to the area covered ! A fascinating variety of dry grassland occurs on small mounds, surrounded by peatland, in hay meadows at Lusmagh, and Banagher, in pasture on the Little Brosna and probably elsewhere. The Oatgrasses are supplemented in these places by a third - DOWNY OATGRASS *Avenula pubescens*. The flowers present on these mounds are reminiscent of the thin calcareous soils of the grassland on the tops of eskers and these are possibly 'outliers' of glacial material - the dry equivalent of the calcareous spring communities. LADY'S MANTLE *Alchemilla* sp., MOUNTAIN EVERLASTING - an unlikely sounding name for a flower on the Callows - *Antennaria dioica*, and even, at the Little Brosna mound, YELLOW-WORT *Blackstonia perfoliata* and FRAGRANT ORCHID *Gymnadenia conopsea*.

Postscript to the flora

There is, of course, ample scope for 'amateurs' and 'professionals' alike to discover species and associations of species new to the Callows. Most of the plant species in this chapter are spread widely, though some sparsely, throughout the Callows from north to south. A detailed study of their distribution might say otherwise. Three other plant species seem to me (unscientifically) to be analogous to scarce or vagrant birds. I found my one and only plant of BROOKWEED *Samolus valerandi* on the mud of a drain which had been silting for twenty-five years just weeks before it was cleaned out and deepened. The only drooping Fritillary-like flowers of WATER AVENS *Geum rivale* I have come across were in torchlight while counting Corncrake. The SHOREWEED *Littorella uniflora* is an underwater plant of stony lakeshores. It is abundant in Lough Ree and Lough Derg. In the River Shannon

Illus. 4.20 Summer Snowflake on the Little Brosna callows. (Photo: S. Heery)

between, which "contrives to flow as a sort of moving lake" (12) Shoreweed was present in 1992 on the gravelly banks of the esker crossing by the bridge at Shannonbridge where it was recorded twenty years ago. (J. Ryan)) and in exactly the same situation at Banagher bridge. This account of the flora of the Callows ends with this strange-flowered plant, an exception rather than a rule.

Illus. 4.22 Marsh Stitchwort
Stellaria palustris
Photo: S. Heery

Illus. 4.21 Reed Canary grass and Common Spike Rush

In certain conditions of high fertility caused by frequent spreading of alluvium by the river, a striking large-scale pattern of blue-green Reed Canary Grass and dark green Common Spike Rush can occur, seen here in the dawn sunlight on the Callows. (Photo: S. Heery)

How can the Callows keep the long list of plant species?

Of the rich variety of plant-life which have found and kept a place in the Callows habitats since they were reclaimed from fen woodland hundreds of years ago, the occurrence of over one hundred and twenty has been described in this chapter. The rest are either listed in Appendix 1 or are waiting to be discovered: under, or emerging from, the waters of the River or drains; soaked in lime-rich water of springs; amongst Reeds; on wet gravel banks; or within the thousands of acres of pasture and hay meadow rising from the low Wigeon-grazed fields to the flood-free rises.

The communities described are what might be called the most 'natural', showing what appears to be the greatest variety of plant species the habitat will allow. Agricultural grassland scientists do not, as a rule, bother too much with semi-natural swards these days, but many years of ordinary management - unrecorded, unintentional management 'experiments' - by farmers have resulted in obvious imbalances of species in some Callows fields. MARSH RAGWORT *Senecio aquaticus* can spread an unwelcome sea of yellow across a 'marshy grassland' pasture; deceptively, on the peatlands, the grass YORKSHIRE FOG *Holcus lanatus*, whose softly hairy leaves are thoroughly disliked by cattle, can dominate and spoil the pasture. An invasion of SOFT RUSH *Juncus effusus* can do the same. In the low-lying grasslands CURLED DOCK *Rumex crispus* can spring up in over-abundance,

remaining ungrazed and providing food for wildfowl, not cattle. On the dry grasslands, HARD RUSH *Juncus inflexus* suppresses grasses and flowers alike. The very basic fact that water-levels and the nature of the land have discouraged reseeding has ensured the survival of semi-natural grassland with its patchwork of grassland conditions - a patchwork enhanced by the fact that over six hundred farmers manage their own small areas of callowland in their own way. Only an unprecedented coincidence would make them all do the same thing at the same time.

Within this agricultural framework several things would lessen the rich variety of plant-life on the Callows. On the grazed and mown grasslands sustained and effective application of 'bag' fertiliser favours a few preferred grasses (Rye Grass, Timothy Grass, Cock's Foot Grass) at the expense of a large variety of grasses, flowers and sedges. Fertiliser application is probably just behind the leading edge of the conflict between agriculture and botanical conservation (the leading edge is ploughing). If cattle were to graze the old meadows throughout the summer, some plants would disappear from these fields, shocked by the continuous cropping. However, grazing a hay meadow, after the species-rich bales have been cleared and a fine, late summer has allowed good regrowth on a dry soil, can help maintain the mixture of species by suppressing the growth of grasses.

Down at the edge of nutrient-rich (eutrophic) waters, such as these, an orderly transition occurs from marsh and tall sedges through to reeds; then 'forests' of rooted aquatics and free-floating plants and, if the water is clear enough, a 'meadow' of submerged plants which rarely have contact with the air. Physical disturbance can destroy the quiet balance - animals grazing the marsh and reeds at the water's edge, boat traffic causing turbulence, nineteenth century navigation works. Plants in this environment soon run out of light at depth and any artificial starving of light through peat suspension and settling, or the addition of even more (artificial) nutrients (agricultural run-off) causing unnatural 'blooms' of algae and microscopic plant-life, impoverishes the aquatic flora. It is not suprising then that the quiet backwaters, especially those adjacent to hay meadows, show the most complete aquatic plant communities (see Map 6)

Drains have an extra dimension. They are designed to carry water and cannot do so if choked with plants. Much has been written about the best way to keep drains functional while keeping a healthy aquatic flora. In general, light and relatively frequent clearing without breaking the 'hard bed' of the drain, and freedom from pollution is best. Here again the six hundred farmers and hundreds of miles of drains ensure that the full range of conditions occur, from recently cleared to choked. Seeds and other propagules lying in the silted bottom of the drain, spread by birds, or floating downstream, mean an ever-changing pattern of diverse aquatic flora, from thin waving Pondweeds to robust Reed Sweetgrass.

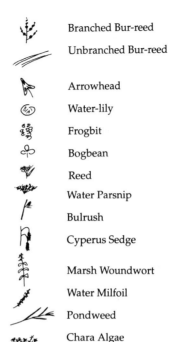

Branched Bur-reed

Unbranched Bur-reed

Arrowhead

Water-lily

Frogbit

Bogbean

Reed

Water Parsnip

Bulrush

Cyperus Sedge

Marsh Woundwort

Water Milfoil

Pondweed

Chara Algae

Illus. 4.23 River-side plant species in a quiet backwater on the Shannon.

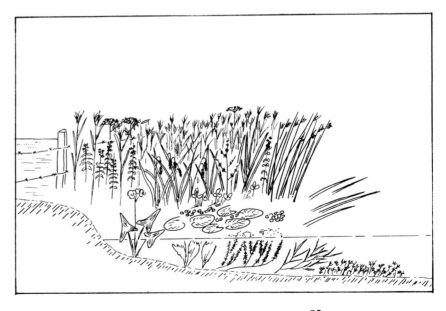

Illus. 5.1 Little Brosna in November 1977.
(Photo: Oscar Merne)

CHAPTER 5

"Skylarks and Corncrakes are often heard"

Birds of the Callows

Diversity through the seasons

Midwinter, and the skies above are overcast or frosty blue. Wildfowl and wading birds of many forms and size have come from widely different lands, north-west and north-east, to spend half the year feeding within the safety of the Callows. The scene is not unlike the thawing tundra to where some will return, but it is quite unlike the hills of Britain to where others will depart. On parts of the Callows they feed without rancour in such numbers that it might be supposed they always live together, instead of dispersing across five thousand miles of the globe.

March and April, and the floods are slow to leave the Callows. Although some of the wintering birds have gone, many are still around building up reserves of energy for the long journey to their breeding grounds. Amongst these come wading birds which

llus. 5.2 Skylark by Gordon D'Arcy 1992

The SKYLARK is a familar bird on the Callows with its constant song while in high vertical flight, and its 'parachuting' down into the grass. Perhaps because it is so familiar it often escapes attention and its status on the Callows is not accurately known. Elsewhere in Ireland it is very dependent on semi-natural grassland on hillsides, sand-dunes etc and any increase in intensification on the Callows would see a decrease in this familiar bird.

intend to lay eggs on the Callows. They don't crowd the place but arrange themselves over the ample expanse of the drying grassland. The Corncrake arrives invisibly to lay its ever more important eggs among the growing flowers and grasses. Other birds pass through.

August, and however the weather has affected human operations on the Callows, most of the birds have finished their breeding attempts, and almost no time elapses before the first of the winter birds arrive in small parties. The first 'laughing' geese are heard very early in October and spiral down to announce the return of winter to the Callows. Numbers of migratory wildfowl and waders build slowly up towards mid-winter.

Breeding Birds on the Callows

The original swamp woodland must have been filled with the songs of small birds. Today, birds of farmland and wood which nest in trees, bushes or tangled undergrowth find few places on the Callows to nest. The only place where the author of 'The Magic of the Shannon' (l) heard a memorable "melody of birdsong" was at Meelick, beyond the sound of the weir and within sight of the ancient Abbey. Here are the wooded 'Scrubby Islands' fringed by a tangle of willows reminiscent of the former swamp woodlands. The song of a Blackcap also rises among wet alder woodland opposite Shannonbridge Power Station and Whitethroats are heard at Shannon Harbour. When Ussher made a trip up the Shannon in 1904, the song of the Willow Warbler (it was then called the Willow Wren) enlivened the river, even where there was hardly a willow to hold the bird.

R.J. USSHER ON THE CALLOWS IN 1904

"Travelling by boat up the Shannon from Banagher to Athlone, one sees an almost uninhabited country. There are no extensive swamps nor reedbeds, but the broad river flows between green 'callows' which are meadowed in summer and often flooded in winter, with boundless high red turf-bogs on the Galway and Roscommon side, and in places on the Eastern side too. Trees are scarce or absent.

The most noticeable bird is the Curlew, which is frequently seen feeding on the river bank or flying to and fro; it breeds on the great red bogs. Redshanks are also numerous; they nest on the callows, which are full of meadowsweet. As the boat proceeds, the Common Sandpiper starts from many a point with its clear cry, and wings its way across the gliding flood. At several places, chiefly above Banagher, I saw Dunlins in breeding plumage busily catering for their mates or young. Black-headed gulls occurred all the way along the River but not in large numbers. They have breeding colonies on the Westmeath bogs. Coots were numerous, and Dabchicks repeatedly met with, and here and there a Heron. I saw one being chased vehemently by a Lapwing from its breeding ground. Skylarks and Corncrakes are often heard, and Reed Buntings several times, while Swifts were frequently dashing past. The song of the Willow-wren, more than any other sound, enlivened this lonely river even in parts where there was hardly a willow to hold the bird.

The stately round towers and ruined churches of Clonmacnoise overlook the great waterway and its wilderness of turf-bogs and here was seen a Corn Bunting, a bird not often met with in the interior. Near Athlone, a Lesser Black-back was on the river, it is partial to the vicinity of the river towns on account of the offal to be got there.

The largest river in the British Isles, with its great lake expansions, was, until twelve years ago, as unknown to me as it is to many a naturalist and tourist even in our own island; but since 1892 I began exploring Lough Derg and Lough Ree I have become familiar with aspects of birdlife almost absent from eastern and southern parts of Ireland." (1904) (28)

But the essence of the dawn chorus on the open Callows fields in spring is its own unique sound of nesting wading birds (described variously as ringing, yelping, yodelling, urgent, plaintive and melancholy) - sounds which stay in the ears and are not easily forgotten.

Songbirds

SKYLARKS (Illus. 5.2) and MEADOW PIPITS are abundant and vocal over the meadows and pastures where they feed and nest. Meadow Pipits are favourite hosts for the parasitic Cuckoo's eggs and Callows pipits, not immune to such bad fortune, were recently seen feeding young Cuckoos. REED BUNTINGS are commonly seen, calling from the branches of willow trees.

Of the small birds, SEDGE WARBLERS (Illus. 5.3) are the most common summer visitor, 'an Irish nightingale' singing from any rank vegetation, reedswamp or tall sedge tussocks. The nocturnal calling of the Corncrake is replaced by the dawn chorus of the Sedge Warbler. GRASSHOPPER WARBLERS can sometimes be heard 'reeling' at dawn or night, and breed throughout the Callows, often on the ground in hay meadows. In 1992 they were particularly widespread in June. Some of those heard in early May could, however, be just passing through, rather like the presence of a WHEATEAR by the same stone wall on the Callows at Shannon Harbour at the end of April 1987 and 1992. These were, perhaps, on their way to Greenland. WHINCHATS occur at Clonmacnoise, on both sides of the river, and elsewhere, nesting in the ungrazed and uncut Purple Moor grass and Cock's Foot grass (2).

Illus. 5.3 Sedge Warbler by Gordon D'Arcy 1992

The commonest summer migrant on the Callows, the SEDGE WARBLER arrives in mid-April and leaves for Africa around the end of August. Its sustained song from reedbeds or rush-infested fields often starts before dawn, earning it the title "Irish Nightingale".

Illus. 5.4 Heron. (Photo: Richard T. Mills)

Pairs of STONECHATS are not common on the Callows in summer, but can be seen in places along the embankment south of Meelick (not in its usual gorse, bracken and stone wall surroundings but calling from willows along a main drain) and from gorse on the fringes of the Little Brosna Callows.

Waterbirds

HERONS (the 'Cranes' of the Callows) (Illus. 5.4) hunt for fish and frogs at the water's edge, often an exciting picture for passing boat travellers whom the birds seem to ignore. Herons do not nest on the Callows , but in colonies in trees. There are two 'heronries' within five miles of Meelick.

MALLARDS will make their nests in the hay meadows, laying eggs in early spring while the meadows are still wetland, and their ducklings have long been taken to the river before the hay is mown.

Since 1984 SHOVELERS have been seen to breed on the Callows. Shovelers are rare breeding ducks in Ireland (3). In 1863 G.H. Kinahan, while thinking of ways to relieve the Shannon of its flooding, "first announced its breeding in this country, near Portumna" and at the end of that century Shoveler were said to be breeding near Banagher (4) (where they still nest today) and the "neighbouring River Brosna". They can be seen, sometimes in pairs before nesting begins in April or May, and later a solitary male in the vicinity of the nest. In 1987 an estimated fourteen pairs nested and since then ducklings, nests and predated eggs have all been seen (Illus. 5.5). Shovelers nest in rough grassland near areas of water and wet mud where they find food and safety. TEALS, TUFTED DUCKS, and even PINTAILS have also been reported as breeding in the 1980s (5).

On the Callows edge, among the reeds, the silent GREAT-CRESTED GREBES nest in low numbers probably because of the relative

Illus. 5.5 Shoveler duck and young by Gordon D'Arcy 1992

The spring and summer activity of bird-life on the Callows centres around the necessity to raise at least one or two young successfully. A female SHOVELER (a rare breeding bird in Ireland) leads her ducklings into the reeds - an essential success because in a subsequent year all her eggs were lost to a fox. The male is a colourful white, chestnut, green and blue.

absence of underwater plants, on which they feed, in the main River. By the same token the unmistakeable 'whinneying trill' of the LITTLE GREBE is common only from the reedbeds and backwaters south of Meelick. MUTE SWANS nest among the reeds with at least a pair every two kilometres. After very high floods in April their nests can be left high and dry, but not abandoned, far from the River.

MOORHENS are widespread, and COOTS less so. Two other members of the Rail familiy, Water Rail and Corncrake, nest in quite opposite kinds of Callows habitats; both are rarely seen, yet both are unmistakeable when heard. It is difficult to know how many WATER RAILS are present in the reeds, callows edges and in the wet, overgrown drainage ditches. Black chicks have been seen

Illus. 5.6 A Corncrake calling on the Callows at Shannonbridge in 1992 (Photo: Richard T. Mills)

Illus. 5.7 Corncrake with mate by Gordon D'Arcy 1992

The CORNCRAKE is a bird on the verge of extinction, with perhaps half the Irish birds nesting in the Callows hay meadows (94 calling birds in 1992). It arrives from Africa in the second half of April and leaves at the beginning of September. It faces unintentional destruction during mowing in June and July. Financial aid needs to be given urgently to farmers to encourage 'Corncrake-friendly' mowing methods, although it must be acknowledged that many Callows farmers voluntarily carried out such methods in the summer of 1992.

recently at Shannon Harbour, and the strange, unearthly squealing of adult birds are reported on the Little Brosna (6) and elsewhere. Farmers walking the fields probably hear many more at many points along the river. Three Water Rails were heard simultaneously within 20 m at Shannon Harbour in early March 1991. Were these winter visitors or did they reflect a breeding density ? South of Meelick, where reedbeds grow par excellence, perhaps two per 100m are heard in August. Five pairs nested among 196 hectares of callowland at Shannon Harbour in 1992.

CORNCRAKES on the Callows

The Corncrake (Illus. 5.6) is a bird on the verge of extinction. At the time of writing (1992) the craking of Corncrakes can still be heard on still June nights from the roadbridge at Banagher in view of the lights of the town; at Shannonbridge above the noise of the peat-fired Power Station; from the ancient monastic buildings at Clonmacnoise; and at points between.

Decline in the past, and present status

The Shannon Callows have become a focus of attention for Corncrake conservation recently with the realisation (in 1988) that about one sixth of Ireland's population of the birds was calling and nesting every year in the hayfields here. If a wider view is taken, so that the whole of Central, Southern, and Western Europe's forty million square kilometres can be seen, then the best estimate put one fiftieth of Europe's Corncrakes in the eight square kilometres of the Callows hay meadows. Totals in the country have declined since, so that in 1992 the Callows probably held a majority of the Irish Corncrakes.

There has been great public interest in the Corncrake since the Irish Wildbird Conservancy surveyed its population in 1978 and again in 1988 (7,8). Accounts of the Corncrakes' rapid and catastrophic decline in Europe and in Ireland, to its final listing by the International Council for Bird Preservation (I.C.B.P) as endangered, can be found elsewhere (3). The general reader can do no better than to read the account in 'The Irish Wildlife Book' (9).

The Corncrake is a member of the Rail family and is sometimes called the Land-rail. This is because, unlike the two closely related birds with which it shares the Callows - the Moorhen at the open water's edge and the Water-rail in dense reeds - the Corncrake is not truly a wetland bird. It is migratory and winters in south-east Africa. After its flight to Ireland it rarely flies and is therefore rarely seen. If a glimpse is caught then its broad chestnut wings, trailing legs, and Mistle Thrush size will distinguish it from a Pheasant, Snipe or Quail

(Illus. 5.7). They arrive in April and seek out long vegetation in which to hide and call before choosing a nest site. The nest is a grass-lined scrape on the ground ('a swirl of grass'), ten or twelve eggs are usually laid which take about sixteen days to hatch. The downy black chicks fend for themselves a few days after hatching and it is another five weeks before they can fly. The female will lay a second clutch if there is time.

It has been shown that Corncrakes heard calling during the latter half of May through to July are not far away from their nest (perhaps 50 m) and stay in its vicinity while calling in order to claim a territory for itself (10). That study also proved what, of course, Irish people over the age of forty already suspected from sleepless experience - that many more Corncrakes call much more often in the middle of the night. During the day the males roam quite widely around the hay fields, picking up, among other things, slugs, weevils and seeds.

The Callows' Corncrakes

The Callows Corncrakes almost exclusively nest in, and call from, the hay meadows of which there is an extensive and relatively unchanging area. Corncrakes spend their time on the Callows between the stems of the hay meadow. In April, when they arrive, they find uncut areas beneath willows or along dilapidated fence-lines, fast growing Canary Grass and Reed Sweetgrass, bog margins or even beneath hedges, where such exist, on the Callows edge. They arrive silently and invisibly and it seems they don't make themselves known until they can call from close to a respectable nesting site. Between 1987 and 1992 at Shannon Harbour the first calling birds were all heard between 17th April and 30th April. In 1991, when the floods were extraordinarily high, an anxious and comprehensive search for calling Corncrakes between Lusmagh and Shannonbridge revealed nothing until 26th April. Where were the silent birds before that time ?

The population of the Shannon Callows Corncrakes has been surveyed from 1988 to 1992. Counting Corncrakes on the Shannon is at once easy and difficult. While the male is making itself known to females and rival males, crex-crexing all night, it is also revealing itself to those who are counting. However, the sometimes tortuous accessibility, the necessity to walk towards each bird in order to pinpoint its position within a large block of haymeadow and the short census time of three hours per night make demands on time and observerpower. As Corncrakes are found in virtually every hay meadow at present an important side product of counting Corncrake is that the continued extent of these meadows can be monitored simultaneously - a cheaper, more down to earth and more reliable way than using satellite images and aerial photography.

In 1987 Corncrakes were counted in passing at the less than optimum time of dawn during a breeding wader survey; in 1988, 1991 and 1992 the whole of the Callows from the Little Brosna to Athlone was counted; and in 1989 and 1990 the section between Banagher and Clonburren was systematically covered.

Table 2 Numbers of calling Corncrakes on the Callows (11)		
	Total Callows	Banagher to Clonburren
1988	125	61
1989		85
1990		62
1991	103	58
1992	94	68

The numbers of Corncrakes are decreasing on the Callows as elsewhere. The decline has been about 6% per year in four years since 1988, a similar situation to the Scottish birds, but much less severe than the 50% crash reported from north-west Ireland.

The decline of Corncrake numbers throughout the country during the past decades has certainly been felt on the Shannon Callows as well. The numbers we hear today, even though they represent a significant population relative to the European one, are low compared to even two decades ago. The maximum possible density of Corncrakes in a meadow is not known. On the Westmeath border of the Callows in the late 1960s 'two birds per acre' were reported (7). This was probably an exaggeration, although it accords with some other local accounts of former Corncrake density in the country. Recent workers on the Callows suggest that sixteen pairs in the 110 ha of hay at Shannon Harbour in 1992 may be close to the maximum, giving about seven hectares to each calling male. If this is the case then in 1988 the 800 ha of Callows' meadows may indeed have been full, with 125 calling birds - the decline not yet started. In the early 1970s one observer recalls hearing 26 along a stretch of callow by Clonown, but it is significant that no-one thought it necessary to actually count them in those days just before the general realisation that a serious decline in numbers was underway. The juxtaposition of two birds - "Skylarks and Corncrakes are often heard" - in Ussher's 1904 day-time account is interesting.

Whatever is the highest number of Corncrakes which the Callows' meadows could support it could be higher than today without the need for extra land being converted to hay. From being as common as a chirping sparrow, it has suddenly become thrilling to stand in a hay meadow on a still June night and listen to the strange call of a Corncrake. But the thrill is dulled by the sight of so many waving silent hectares of grassland from which its companions should be replying. Conservation efforts are aimed at making two Corncrakes call where once there was one.

How can the Callows keep their Corncrakes ?

As in so many other aspects of the Callows their Corncrakes surprise even the experts. Workers from the Royal Society for the Protection of Birds, visiting the Callows in 1991, had never heard so many Corncrakes calling at once. In 1991 the Corncrakes calling on the Callows were counted as usual at night by volunteers who found them to number one hundred and three. In addition, Corncrakes were 'watched' very closely for the first time by a full-time field worker and there were plans in 1992 to intensify this scrutiny in a very much more detailed manner.

There is much to be learned about the Corncrake, but the most immediate problems occur at mowing time. Good populations of Corncrakes in Europe remain only where high rainfall or spring flooding do not permit early

Illus. 5.9 A water rail, photo: The National Trust, Ian Herbert.

mowing of hay - Donegal and Mayo, the Shannon Callows, similar floodmeadows in France, and the Western Isles of Scotland. Young chicks have been seen in mid-June and also feeding among the standing Callows hay in the late-August. Farmers on the Callows will always avoid harming them if they are seen at mowing time. But the bird's secretive behaviour (nests are almost impossible to find and mark), and its biological abhorrence to crossing open ground, makes unavoidable and unintentional mortality a sad reality.

Cutting a field of hay from the centre outwards gives flightless chicks a chance to move away from the mowing machine to the safety of the next field or fence-line. Slower speeds obviously help in the process. This is an unconventional, more awkward and time-consuming way of farming. Nevertheless many farmers on the Callows demonstrated their concern in 1992 by attempting this 'Corncrake-friendly' practice (Illus. 5.10).

Successful hay making in a climate like Ireland's depends on timely and speedy decisions. When conditions are right, the whole crop of hay on the Callows can be cut and cleared in two weeks starting at the beginning of July. Where are the chicks and adults on these bare fields - in overgrown drains, fringing hedgerows, reeds at the river's edge ? The chicks especially are trying to hide from predatory Hooded Crows and Gulls.

An ideal Callows Corncrake field is a hay meadow of native plants, cut slowly, from the centre outwards, in late August, with tall uncut places left to hide next year's birds. Callows farmers have small farms. Many would be willing to be especially 'Corncrake-friendly' if grants were available to compensate them for going against long held haymaking instincts to make hay while the sun shines. Conservation organisations in Ireland have all recommended that the Callows be classified by the Government as an 'Environmentally Sensitive Area' (E.S.A. - Chapter 7). But while waiting, with decreasing patience, for this to happen an interim scheme of grants needs to be urgently devised, before the Corncrake population reduces itself to zero.

Conservation attempts at the time of mowing can only be successful if a good proportion of Corncrakes return to the vicinity of birth. Many bird species indeed do this, including the Corncrake's neighbour on the Callows - the Lapwing. How many Callows Corncrake will return ? Their arrival in April 1993 is very anxiously awaited.

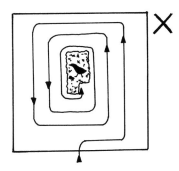

When cutting, please consider trying some of these methods

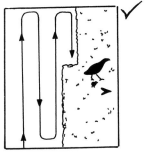

Cut the field in strips from side to side like this.

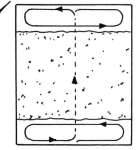

It may be necessary to cut a strip at the top and bottom sections first. This method is suitable for drum/rotary mowers.

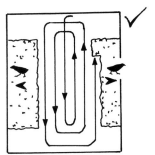

Cut the field from the middle outwards.

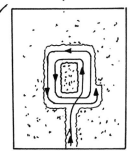

Cut from the gate towards the middle of the field.

Corncrakes
on the
Shannon Callows

Illus. 5 10 'Corncrake-friendly' mowing methods.

This leaflet was produced by the Irish Wildbird Conservancy advising farmers on mowing methods which give the Corncrake a chance of survival. In 1992 quite a number of farmers gave the methods a try and it is known that some birds were saved. (courtesy of Irish Wildbird Conservancy)

Illus. 5.11 Greenland White-fronted Geese

There are only about 23,000 of this type of wild goose in the world, about 12,000 winter in Ireland and about 500 use the Callows (including the Little Brosna) and a further 400 or so use the River Suck callows. The adults are distinguished from other 'grey geese' by their white forehead and black bars and blotches on the breast. (Colour photo: Alyn Walsh)

Illus. 5.12 Lapwing's eggs on the Callows by Anne O'Connell 1992

The LAPWING makes no attempt to hide her eggs, which are laid in a shallow scrape on short grass. Instead, it relies on communal effort and a number of Lapwings will try to drive away a Hooded Crow. If the Lapwing is distracted by a human intruder the Crow will take its chance and steal the eggs. The same applies to Curlew on the Callows. So anyone walking on the Callows must pass on quickly and allow the bird to settle on her eggs once more.

BREEDING WADING BIRDS
on the Callows

A Rare Assemblage

The conservation of Corncrake and the conservation of breeding waders (LAPWING, REDSHANK, SNIPE and CURLEW) represent two extremes in rationale. The first is a bird on the verge of extinction, the others are widespread and generally common in Ireland at present. Lapwing will nest on bare arable fields and grassy moorland; Snipe will nest in soft boggy ground; Curlew will nest on bogs and moorland; Redshank (the most restricted of the four) require rough grassland near water. But the story of the Corncrake reminds us how quickly a common bird can reach the brink of extinction.

However, all four species are attracted to lowland wet grassland in spring and summer to breed, and the Shannon Callows provide the necessary conditions for all four wading species to breed together in numbers equalled by only three places in Britain and Ireland - Erne Basin, Co. Fermanagh; Ouse Washes, Cambridgeshire; and North Kent Marshes, England. In 1987 1,551 pairs were nesting on the 3,500 hectares of the Shannon Callows (12).

The case for conservation efforts for Corncrake on the Callows is self-evident but, in the case of breeding waders, it is the great assemblage of the four species in such numbers which is the rare thing.

The Callows' breeding wading birds

In 1987 Lapwing, Snipe, Redshank and Curlew were present in remarkably even numbers and distribution all along the 35 km length of the Callows from The Little Brosna to Athlone. To the south of Athlone, Snipe were the only abundant species. Over the Callows as a whole just under half the birds were Snipe, with most of the remainder being Lapwing and Redshank in equal proportions. Curlew were present in small numbers throughout.

Table 3 Numbers of wading birds breeding on the Callows in 1987	
LAPWING	341 pairs
REDSHANK	400 pairs
SNIPE	762 pairs
CURLEW	48 pairs

Along each two mile stretch of callowland, Snipe, Lapwing, Redshank and Curlew were nesting in approximately these proportions. Hopefully, they still are, although no subsequent survey has yet been carried out. At one site, Shannon Harbour/Bullock Island (13, and unpublished data) numbers have shown no decline to date (1991):

Illus. 5.14 Heads of four wading birds which nest on the Callows. from left to right: Lapwing, Curlew, Redshank, Snipe.

Each of the four birds are very different in form, behaviour and habitat requirements. Conditions on the Callows combine to allow these birds to nest in numbers equalled only by three other places in Ireland and Britain.

97

Shannon Harbour: no. of pairs of				
	Lapwing	Redshank	Snipe	Curlew
1987	29	26	61	5
1988	39	31	78	6
1989	33	35	123	4
1990	32	34	70	5
1991	32	30	122	9
1992	21	32	76	6

(unpublished, S.Heery, I.J. Herbert, C.R.M. Meredith)

Four very different species

The four species are very different to each other in form, habitat requirements and behaviour, over and on the Callows (Illus 5.14). A casual observer will recognise the Lapwing by its striking black and white appearance, flapping flight on rounded 'top heavy' wings, and plaintive cry. Redshanks are even noisier on their breeding grounds with an urgent piping, rapid direct flight on wings with flashes of white, and bright red beak and legs. The Curlew is the largest of the four but can be remarkably elusive and silent to observe. If it chooses to display, then its immensely long curved bill and a cry like its name will give it away (Illus. 5.15). Snipe cannot be seen on the ground, although they will, rarely, perch incongruously on a telegraph pole or other vantage point more suited to blackbirds. If flushed from cover during the breeding season, the male will fly rapidly up to a great height and perform an aerobatic display in wide circles around its nest site. On a still day, or at dusk, it creates a strangely soothing sound best described by the local name of 'skygoat' or, in a different habitat from the Callows, 'heather bleater'. The sound is referred to as 'drumming' by ornithologists and is a convenient way of counting just how many females are likely to be sitting tightly on nests hidden amongst the rough grass or meadow. It makes this sound by vibrating two outer tail feathers with rushing air during its aerobatics (Illus. 5.16).

Densities

In the natural world different species in a stable community do not compete with each other for the things they need to live. They can only exist side by side if they are using different parts of the habitat or if they use the same parts at different times. This is so for Lapwings, Snipe, Redshanks and Curlews on the Callows. It allows them to breed side by side in the fields, a nest every two hectares along the whole stretch of callowland. On Inishee there were two nests for every one hectare of the island in 1987.

How do these birds divide time, space and food on the Callows ?

The timing of breeding is different.

Lapwings are the earliest to start breeding on the Callows and their eggs can be laid in late-March. By mid-April and into early May the chicks have hatched and are running around the field protected from dogs, foxes, hooded crows, falcons and hawks by courageous parents (Illus. 5.17). By the beginning of June most have finished breeding attempts and those chicks that have survived the natural hazards (it may be only one out of three) are looking like scruffy adults and are flocking together with them. A flock of 125 was seen in early June in 1987. A mid-August flock of 800 on the Little Brosna callows in 1991 had possibly been joined for the winter by birds from Britain and the Continent.

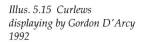

Illus. 5.15 Curlews displaying by Gordon D'Arcy 1992

The numbers of breeding CURLEW on the Callows today is small, but significant. In the past many more Curlews were to be seen, although many of these nested on the adjacent bogs which, before large-scale harvesting for peat in the 1950s, provided thousands of hectares of perfect nesting sites. The male performs an intense territorial display over the callows, gliding with arched wings and haunting cry. They are otherwise unobtrusive.

Illus. 5.16 Snipe 'drumming' by Gordon D'Arcy 1992

The SNIPE is the commonest nesting wading bird on the Callows with probably over one thousand pairs nesting following a late fall of the floods in April. The male performs his famous 'drumming' display in wide circles over the nest-site by diving with two splayed tail feathers vibrating in the rush of air. The sound, especially at twilight, is strangely soothing, and not completely conveyed by its local name of 'skygoat'.

At a time when the first Lapwing chicks are hatching, in late April, the Snipe are just beginning to breed. The male does a 'wing-arching' display at this time just before egg-laying, when it dives into cover with wings forming an acute V-shape. By the time the Lapwings are flocking, Snipe chicks are being followed around by their parents. Snipe have another timing strategy different from Lapwings. As a response to nest loss by predators, flooding or being stepped on by cattle, Snipe will nest again and again until July.

LAPWINGS will defend their chicks against predators, but in fact they will mob a KESTREL in or out of the breeding season. The tables are turned when the Kestrel's larger relative, the Peregrine Falcon, appears. The Lapwing is then not safe from this powerful falcon's 'stoop' and headlong chase across the callows.

They choose different details of the Callows character for their nest-sites.

Lapwings make a scrape in the ground in the shortest of vegetation or even in patches devoid of plants altogether (Illus. 5.12). They like to see an intruder from a distance and feed close to the nest on invertebrates picked off the

Redshanks time their breeding in a similar way to Snipe except that they do not have the capacity for repeated nesting attempts and in fact leave for their coastal wintering grounds in late-June whether or not they have raised young without mishap.

Curlews are slower in their breeding cycle than either Snipe or Redshanks and consequently are still to be seen watching over foraging chicks when most of the Callows are silent of the sounds of other breeding waders in-late July.

Illus. 5.18 Redshank on post by Gordon D'Arcy 1992

Almost one seventh of the Irish population of REDSHANKS nest on the Shannon Callows. A fence post is a favourite place for the male to stand watch for its mate sitting on eggs closeby. No intruder can come near without this 'sentinel of the marshes' piping its warning.

ground. This makes a sitting or feeding Lapwing a very conspicuous black and white speck on the Callows for avian, human or other mammalian observers. But they are rarely found nesting alone and rely on communal effort to drive away predators. Conditions for nesting Lapwings are normally found in a pasture which has been well-grazed just before the winter floods, but a few find conditions suitable in hay meadows. Growth in the meadows early in the season is not rapid and the sitting birds are not obscured.

Redshank are very difficult to detect when sitting on eggs. Their nest is a grass-lined, hollowed-out tuft of grass or sedge, hidden by a canopy of blades. Birds that are not sitting can be seen some distance away feeding in wet mud or standing guard on a fence post close to the nest (Illus. 5.18). Their chicks have a particular requirement of feeding in water where they will wade into what seems to be dangerously deep water although waders can, in fact, swim. They probably do not come across the chicks of their companion waders in this situation.

Snipe feed by probing their beaks into soft mud and feeling for invertebrates with the tips of their beaks. This tip will open independently to the rest of the beak allowing it to pick up food from a depth. Snipe also hide their eggs in a nest with a woven canopy of leaves, and the sitting female likes to walk off the nest to feed. This restricts the nest-site to areas of soft or damp soil when they begin to nest in late-April. If the ground becomes too hard to probe with their beaks they will cease their repeated nesting attempts. They will choose nest-sites in hay or pasture equally.

The sitting Curlew and her eggs is too big to hide and relies on camouflage, silence and the growing meadow around it for protection.

How many of these birds were breeding on the Callows in the past is mostly speculation. A resident of Banagher, living on the edge of the Callows, tells of abundant Lapwings in fields in which they are now absent. A striking observation on nesting Curlews in 'Birds of Ireland' 1954 is quoted in full.

How can the Callows keep this congregation of breeding waders ?

Each pair of waders needs to rear at least one chick to adulthood, on average, every year in order that the population is sustained. It is presumptuous to claim to know exactly what birds require of their nesting locality but, of course, they need nesting sites, abundant food and minimum disturbance.

A 'COLONY' OF CURLEW' IN 1954

"But the great (Curlew) breeding ground of S. Connaught is the wastes and callows between Banagher and Lough Derg. Near Portumna, the nests are so close as almost to rank as a colony"
(1954) (25)

Wading birds are not deterred by flooding at their nest-sites in March and April. They are, after all, wading birds with long legs and these are conditions in which they have spent their winter. But the slow drying out of the fields means they have the place to themselves at the most crucial time of their breeding. There are no cattle to tread their eggs and they don't have to run the gauntlet between tractor wheels traversing and fertilising, or worse, rolling the field. Waders (especially Snipe) are positively helped by flooding in spring. The ground is kept soft, and double the numbers of Snipe are likely to choose nest-sites after a late-April, compared to late-March, fall of the River. On land which is managed specifically for breeding waders in other countries, sluices are attached to the outfall of drains to keep water-tables high in the event of low river levels.

All four wader species (but especially Snipe and Redshanks) benefit if the river level hovers within 30cm below ground level in May, with the presence of shallow pools and riverside vegetation. The essential fact that Meelick weir can postpone low river-levels as far as Athlone should not be forgotten in any discussion of the Callows future.

Waders eat large quantities of invertebrates and little is known yet about this on the Callows. It is, however, known that intensification of grassland management descreases the size, abundance and variety of these invertebrate food items. The food for the chicks is probably more important than anything else. They are not fed by their parents and of course they cannot fly to the best feeding places as adults can. From day one they must keep warm under their parents in cold weather, and hide from predators, as well as find enough food. Chicks have to find enough food items within walking distance of their short legs and their requirements change with their growth. The relationship between chicks and earthworms, aphids, midges, flies, beetles and all the other crawling food items is highly complex but whatever the chicks need they are finding it on the Callows at present. It can be assumed that any increase in intensification, decribed in chapter 6, will make the Callows less attractive to these birds.

Even on the Callows as they exist today the breeding waders have to contend with many difficulties. In habitats created and managed specially for breeding waders in the Netherlands, up to twenty Lapwings will join forces to challenge a Crow intent on stealing eggs from a nest. On the Callows one or two take up the challenge and the Crow will often win. Lapwings and Curlews, their eggs in exposed nests, are particularly and successfully harassed by the predators of eggs. Redshanks and Snipe, their eggs hidden, fare better. Snipe, which choose an ideal nest-site in ground which is soft in early-April after the winter floods, can have difficulty probing for food in ground near the nest which has become too hard for them in June.

It is almost inevitable that places like the Callows will become increasingly important in a countryside of shrinking wetlands. In the future, if the highly complex issues of river-levels in spring, recreation, and farming can be overcome, wading birds could be encouraged to breed in even greater numbers on the Callows.

Some other birds

COMMON SANDPIPERS, summer migrants, somewhat related to the Redshank, breed on the banks of the river. In 1987 twenty-two pairs held territories along contiguous stretches of the river bank from Bishop's Islands to Athlone, advertising their presence with a high-pitched trill over the water and a Redshank-like waggling of white-barred wings. Common Sandpipers like stones in a river on which to be conspicuously territorial, and along this stretch they use glacial boulders and gravels occurring naturally or dredged up last century during the Shannon Navigation improvement works. Typical locations are Derryholmes and Devenish Island (Illus. 3.4). This may account for the density of a pair almost every kilometre, which is thought to be unusually high for a sluggish lowland clay river such as the Shannon. Its more familiar habitat is fast flowing, stony, upland streams or stony lakeshore. They arrive in mid-April and are gone by late-June.

QUAILS, also summer migrants, are rare and rather erratic breeders in Ireland (3)- birds of open grassland, hay meadows and crops (Illus. 5.19) . Every year since 1987 Quail have been

Illus. 5.19 Quail by Gordon D'Arcy 1992

The QUAIL is a rare breeding bird in Ireland, seen here hiding beneath an OXE-EYE DAISY and other dry grassland flowers in a Callows hayfield. In 1989 and 1992 Quails were relatively widespread on the Callows in keeping with a temporary increase throughout the country. But they are strongly suspected to breed in very small but regular numbers on the Callows each year. They are said to be a close companion of the Corncrake during migration and are certainly in just as much danger at mowing time.

heard in the dark by observers counting Corncrakes on Clonburren meadows, and the conclusion must be that the Callows are a regular (unsuspected) breeding site for this small bird. As they do not begin to nest until early-June and even the earliest chicks will not be flying until mid-July, slow and late-cutting in a 'Corncrake-friendly' manner will help this bird as it will all other hay-nesting birds on the Callows. A brood of Quail was destroyed by mowing at Banagher in late-July 1992. In June 1989 the unmistakeable 'whic whic whic' of the calling bird sounded in the air above the Corncrakes at Bishop's Islands and Shannon Harbour. Quail are believed to have bred exceptionally widely in Ireland that year. But again in 1992 the Callows Quail were making themselves heard from Golden Island to Lusmagh (14). The Callows are evidently a regular breeding haunt of this rare, seldom heard and rarely seen migrant.

HOODED CROWS - resident, common and widespread throughout the country - are universally present on the Callows in spring and early summer when the waders are at the height of their breeding. The presence of these sombre grey and black birds is especially significant at a time when eggs and chicks are abundant, and many fall prey. Gangs of non-breeding Hooded Crows are sometimes seen on the Callows (thirty were seen once), possibly attracted by a disturbing increase in sheep carcasses which have appeared on the Callows in recent years. The occasional low tree on the Callows can support a Hooded Crow's nest, well-chosen, surrounded by food for its own fledglings. When a Hooded Crow steals an egg from a nest it flies some distance to a favourite place at which to pick a hole in the shell and drink its contents. The eggs of Moorhen, Coot, Mallard, Lapwing, Redshank, Snipe, and Curlew have all been found in these 'caches' on the Callows.

Other predators stalk the Callows in summer. A Fox has been seen with a mouthful of Mallard, and the islands do not deter them. Mink are evidently widespread in the Midlands and have been seen on the River at Meelick. They will take eggs and young, and in Britain have been known to cause desertion of a site by breeding waders. Otters, although generally fish-eaters, will take chicks if stumbled upon. Otters have been seen among the Callows grassland on two separate occasions (Ballymacegan and Clonburren). Otter and Mink tracks occurred together on the banks of the Little Brosna. A Redshank carcass in a Callows-edge thicket had been taken there by a Sparrowhawk.

Postscript to the Breeding Birds

If time is taken to think of all the birds nesting on the ground amongst all the hay and pasture of the Callows (Mallard, Shoveler, Quail, Water Rail, Corncrake, Lapwing, Snipe, Redshank, Curlew, Skylark, Meadow Pipit, Grasshopper Warbler) it will be realized that almost every hectare houses a breeding bird or its young during May to August. All these can be found in the hay meadows and all are as vulnerable as the Corncrake to destruction during the trauma at mowing time. 'Corncrake-friendly' mowing must be seen as the saviour of all ground-nesting birds on the Callows (see Table 1).

A mammal on the Callows

Good views of the Irish Hare (the common hare in Ireland - a distinct race of the Scottish Mountain or Blue Hare, not the Brown Hare of England) can sometimes be seen on the Callows. It will run, foxy-coloured, maybe splashing through shallow floods, pausing upright now and again, ignoring the drains, until it is a speck on the green fields. One story of the Irish Hare on the Callows is both suprising and disturbing. Until the early 1980s hares were "plentiful" companions to the breeding birds on the narrow-necked island of Inishee, near Banagher. A paradise for hares in summer, but in winter all but a tiny part of the island is under flood. Hares must have regularly swum on and off the island like the cattle that graze it. Hares are scarce or absent on the island now. They were not beaten by the floods but by the shape of the island. Men whose sport was hare-coursing came from a distance onto the island to drive the hares towards the narrow neck where they were caught in nets and transported to coursing fields further south. This was the 1980s, not the 1880s.

WINTERING BIRDS
on the Callows

As a winter destination for wildfowl and waders breeding from Greenland to Siberia, and in continental Europe, the Shannon Callows are second to none and their lateral extension, the Little Brosna callows, has provoked superlatives from ornithologists.

"...one of the most magnificent places in Ireland to watch great flocks of wildfowl" 1979 (15)

*Map 7
Winter attraction of the callows to birds*

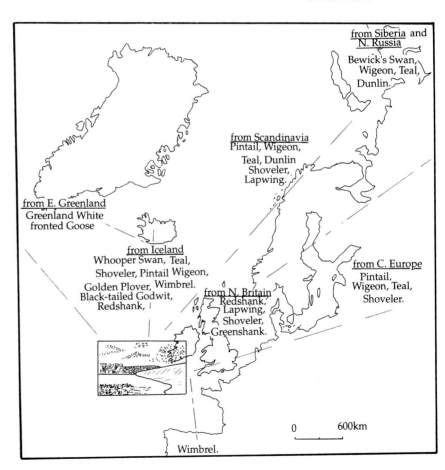

" ...the hub of waterbird activity in Ireland." 1982 (16)

" This phenomenal site recalls what must have been commonplace throughout Europe but is now almost gone - a highly productive floodplain, enriched by wildfowl in winter and cropped for hay or grazed in summer" 1991 (17)

Numbers of 'international significance'

General visitors to the Callows, in the right place at the right time, do not need to know just how many make up the spectacle of birds displaying before them. But, nonetheless, numbers are important in the conservation of nature. It was recently shown that fifteen main waterbird species involving almost 30,000 wildfowl and 30,000 wading birds can be present on the 3,500 hectares of Shannon Callows in general, with half of these crowding into the 800 hectares of the Little Brosna (17).

Counting the actual numbers of these birds is notoriously difficult, not least on the Callows. Even without disturbance there is a constant movement of birds to and fro within a site in front of the observer. Flocks of wildfowl and, especially, dense flocks of waders have to be estimated without warning. Furthermore, on such a linear expanse of habitat as the Callows there can be daily movement along flight lines which extend along the whole 50km stretch. Many parties, large and small, of all species can be found at all points along the river, so accurate counting can only be done from the air. Movement in response to flooding conditions also occurs. As most wildfowl feed in shallow water, or at the flood's edge, water levels can either be too high or too low for the usual large numbers. Daily and seasonal shooting pressure can have a (largely unassessed) effect on the birds' whereabouts.

Nevertheless, two large-scale censuses involving many counts at different times during the winters 1972/73 - 1973/74 and 1984/85 - 1986/87 have been carried out on the Shannon (by Irish Wildbird Conservancy members and staff of the Wildlife Service) and have established the winter Callows as host to populations of WHOOPER SWAN, BEWICK'S SWAN, GREENLAND WHITE-FRONTED GOOSE, WIGEON and BLACK-TAILED GODWIT which have an international significance. Species which occur in numbers which are vital within Ireland (nationally significant) are TEAL, MALLARD, PINTAIL, SHOVELER, MUTE SWAN, GOLDEN PLOVER, LAPWING and CURLEW.

A list of wintering birds on the Shannon Callows is given in Appendix 2.

Birds do not respect international boundaries. For a site to be of 'international importance' to a wintering bird species more than one hundreth of the total north-west European (for wildfowl) and western European (for waders) population must congregate regularly there at any time either as a resident winter population or during migration. For instance, there are thought to be about 750, 000 Wigeon using

Table 4
The most recent census - 1986/1987 (based on 17,18)
An indication of numbers of most numerous birds

	Shannon Callows	Little Brosna Callows	Internationally important threshold	Estimated Irish population
Mute Swan	253	92	1,800	5-7,000
Bewick's Swan*	present	20	170	2,500
Whooper Swan	211	201	170	10,300
White-fronted Goose*	present	417	220	12,000
Wigeon	8,725	12,250	7,500	100-150,000
Teal	900	3,000	4,000	50,000
Mallard	84	2,259	20,000	50,000
Pintail	present	275	700	1-3,000
Shoveler*	16	250	400	8,000
Golden Plover*	4500	5,000	10,000	200,000
Lapwing*	12,865	3,925	20,000	200,000
Dunlin	present	650	20,000	100-130,000
Black-tailed Godwit*	600	2,375	400	8-10,000
Curlew	300	1,150	3,000	150,000

Illus. 5.20 Table 4. An indication of the large numbers of wintering birds on the Callows.

These are the peak numbers seen during four aerial counts of the whole area in the winter of 1986/1987. Ground observation confirms that all species can be found in any part of the Shannon and Little Brosna Callows, sometimes in higher numbers than indicated here, for instance:
* 3,500-4,000 Black-tailed Godwit on Little Brosna, March 2 1991 (G. D'Arcy)
* 3800 Black-tailed Godwit on Little Brosna, January 20 1993 (Paul Galvin)
* 360 Shoveler on Little Brosna, January 5 1993 (PG)
* 470 Greenland White-fronted Goose on Little Brosna, November 11 1992 (PG)
* 8,500 Lapwing on Little Brosna, January 5 1993
* 6,650 Golden Plover on Little Brosna, November 11 1992 (PG)
* up to ten times this number of Bewick's Swans are almost certainly present on the Little Brosna - River Shannon - River Suck callows system as a whole.

north-west Europe in winter and spring, between 100,000 and 150,000 of these winter in Ireland. 12, 000 of these can be present on the Little Brosna callows (17) and perhaps 8000 use the rest of the Shannon Callows at some time during the winter. The case is similar, but more dramatic, for Black-tailed Godwits which breed in Iceland . 2, 000 and sometimes 4, 000 or so of the total population of 40, 000 congregates on the Little Brosna and Shannon Callows especially in spring. Furthermore, a place where twenty thousand waterbirds of any description regularly congregate is recognised as being of 'international importance'.

Icelandic birds

It has been speculated that in late-February and early-March the Shannon Callows take on special significance for Irish birds bound for breeding grounds in Iceland (18). While Wigeon, Shovelers and Teal in the rest of the country are leaving for northern Europe, birds bound for Iceland were thought to be swelling the numbers to a peak on the Callows. They joined the Whooper Swans, Black-tailed Godwits, Golden Plovers, and possibly Pintail taking in energy from the rich Callows feeding for their journey north-west to Iceland. The account of the most recent census (17) suggests that this congregation of Icelandic birds (at least, the Wigeon) on the Callows may not be so significant. There are many unknowns in the natural world. Fast flocks of Teal, whistling and looking almost black, were still present at Shannon Harbour, accompanied by Golden Plover, in mid-April 1992.

The island of Iceland is outstanding for breeding wildfowl and waders whose populations depend upon winter refuges further south. The Shannon Callows are a correspondingly outstanding winter refuge.

The past and future

But, like the Corncrake and probably breeding waders, the 'spectacular' concentrations of wildfowl we see today are nothing to what was seen even well within living memory. Callows "black with geese" are remembered before the harvesting of the Blackwater Bog complex started in the late-1950s, an observation which stretched back into last century (19). If the Callows ever became unsuitable as a waterbird refuge it is unlikely that other sites in the area or even in the country could absorb such large numbers. Similarly, if any part of the Callows became unsuitable then the remainder would be diminished. The whole wetland area comprising the Shannon - Little Brosna - Suck, along with subsidiary sites, is one whole wildfowl complex.

On the other hand, an opportunity exists to enhance and increase the wildfowl of the Shannon area by management of cutaway bogs, especially Blackwater Bog. (see chapter 7)

None of these birds is, of course, exclusive to the Callows. All of them occur in even greater numbers at a few, mostly coastal sites (illustrated graphically in the maps of 'Ireland's Wetlands and their Birds'). But for a site far inland to provide the undisturbed space and productivity to rival the vastness of estuaries at low tide is indeed special. In fact, in the 1970s, when the first official account of winter bird numbers on the Little Brosna callows was reported, the place was actually referred to as the Little Brosna Estuary. Whoever coined the phrase had the correct image of a river, at times heavily laden with sand and silt, meeting the ocean-like Shannon floods, enriching the land with its deposits. However, the term has not endured.

The Birds

Ireland's two wintering wild swans join each other on the Callows each from different parts of the globe. The BEWICK'S SWAN is one of Europe's scarcest wildfowl today, but in 1845 birds from the Shannon found their way to the markets of Dublin. The Bewick's local name is 'Russian goose' on account of its breeding grounds and its more-goose-than-swan-like shape and size. Bewick's are generally found in small herds, although one hundred and sixty were present at Clonown in February 1970. WHOOPER SWANS (Illus. 5.21) come from breeding grounds in Iceland and large flocks of 60 or so of these, the largest bird in Ireland, can suprise an observer on any part of the Callows. Parties of swans in early September are MUTE SWANS which have bred on the river, along with large numbers of immatures and non-breeders.

At Clonown ". . . the acres that feed the winter swans become an expanse of sweet-scented meadows" (20). In March 1992 a spectacular 250 swans (mostly Whoopers with some Mutes) grazed the green islands of the highest parts of the meadows at Clonown during high flood. When such a sight is seen the origin of the collective name 'a herd of swans' is easily imagined.

The only true Callows goose is the GREENLAND WHITE-FRONTED GOOSE (Illus. 5.11) However, these are accompanied almost yearly by a few Pink-footed Geese, the odd Greylag (both of which winter in small numbers in Ireland, mainly on the coast) and even a Barnacle Goose (a western coastland bird). All these geese pass through Iceland on their way to Ireland and the hangers-on must join the main flocks there. It is irresistible to note that there is a place called Shannon Island within the breeding range of the Pinkfoot and Barnacle Geese on the east coast of Greenland !

The thousand and more Greenland White-fronted Geese which used the Shannon Callows, including the Little Brosna, before the mid-1950s are well-documented in both local memory and the scientific literature. Colourful local impressions bear witness to this abundance: the Callows were sometimes "black with geese" at Shannon Harbour; and geese

Illus. 5.21 Whooper Swans by Gordon D'Arcy 1992

The WHOOPER SWAN is Ireland's largest bird and over 400 migrate from their breeding grounds in Iceland to winter on the Callows. They often make a low-key 'whooping' sound as they feed in small flocks. In some places, notably Clonown, 200 or more can sometimes be seen grazing the flood-free Callows grassland. The collective name 'herd of swans' is then quite easy to understand. The other migratory winter swan on the Callows is the BEWICK'S SWAN. It is quite similar but is smaller, more goose-like in its form, and has less yellow and more black on its beak. Even a practised eye can sometimes have difficulty distinguishing them in a mixed herd.

were said to "queue up" at a favourite place on the close-grazed pasture north of the road at Esker to ingest sand (which wildfowl need to break down food in their gizzard). There were evidently other favourite spots along the Callows for this activity, for instance beneath the high esker hill at Clonmacnoise.

In the 1940s more geese frequented the Shannon than the Little Brosna. Now the situation is reversed. Then, three separate flocks of about 150 each were reported between Athlone and Banagher (Athlone area, Clonown area, and Shannon Harbour area) and about 400 used the Little Brosna area (19). Today, a small flock uses the Shannon, still using all the traditional sites of the former larger flocks, and still 400 or so birds use the Little Brosna. Then, the Callows were only part of their essential habitat, the adjacent but inaccessible bogs of Clonfert, Blackwater and others providing refuge from disturbance and extra-nutritious food in the form of overwintering shoots and other underground parts of the White-beaked Sedge and other bogland plants which store minerals from withering winter leaves.

Now, they feed mostly on the Callows, still probing for underground parts of Callows plants, especially the Jointed Rush and Creeping Buttercup (they pull up the whole plant and discard the leaves), and the stems of White Clover and Creeping Bent Grass. Leaves of Floating Sweetgrass, Bent Grass, Marsh Foxtail and Red Fescue are also grazed. They

must manage to find some feeding on the 500 ha or so of unharvested bogs which are left in their range because the remains of White-beaked Sedge (a bog plant) were found in droppings of geese feeding on the Little Brosna callows (21).

The geese need to spend most of the day selecting highly digestible food plants, and disturbance in any form disrupts this and has consequences on site desertion, mortality and even breeding success in distant Greenland (22). On the Shannon Callows agricultural activity and shooting (of other quarry species) in winter, pleasure cruisers, fishing in spring (the birds do not leave for their breeding grounds until mid-April) and an increased popularity and promotion of birdwatching are, or could become, significant causes of disturbance (23).

WIGEON (Illus. 5.22) , with their noisy communal whistling, are perhaps the most characteristic bird of the winter Callows and account for the largest numbers and the most noise during their stay each year. They graze at the edge of the flood, choosing, if possible, places where the soft-leaved creeping grasses are plentiful - Floating Sweetgrass, Creeping Bentgrass and Marsh Foxtail. They can be encountered in parties from fifty to many hundreds throughout the Callows wherever their preferred feeding occurs, wherever the flood is neither too high nor too low for a long strip of edge-of-flood feeding or very shallow water dabbling to be available, and wherever disturbance is minimal. Flooding on the Shannon is usually between the two extremes. Conditions on the Little Brosna combine to allow Wigeon to feed in many thousands.

The principal ducks to accompany Wigeon on the Callows are TEAL and SHOVELER each obtaining something different from the highly productive collection of leaves, seeds, fruits and roots of Callows plants and the insects, snails, worms and other freshwater animals which depend on them. Not all Callows Shoveler are from Iceland. One ringed in the nest in Latvia in 1978 was shot on the Roscommon Shannon Callows the next year. Male PINTAIL (Illus. 5.23) are very conspicuous amongst a congregation of ducks, their pure white fronts shining in the sun.

Illus. 5.22 Wigeon by Gordon D'Arcy 1992

The WIGEON are the most abundant winter duck on the Callows with up to 20,000 being present in large and small flocks over the whole length but concentrating on the Little Brosna callows. They are responsible for a constant 'whistling' sound when large numbers are present. The male has a smooth chestnut head with a buff-yellow crown and short blue bill. They begin to arrive in September (or earlier), build up to a mid-winter peak, which stays high until they leave in March. None stays to breed on the Callows.

Illus. 5.23 Pintail. (photo: Richard T. Mills)

Illus. 5.24 Flock of Golden Plover by Gordon D'Arcy 1992

Tight flocks of GOLDEN PLOVERS numbering thousands can be encountered anywhere on the Callows. Their changing patterns are among the Callows most memorable sights. In winter they are drab brown birds, but before they leave the Callows in spring many have their black-bellied breeding plumage and golden backs.

Parties of up to fifty Pintails can also occur on the Shannon and more are winter residents on the Little Brosna. A young bird ringed in a nest in Murmansk, Russia, in July 1979 (24) made its way to Shannon Harbour in November the same year. Also at Shannon Harbour in March 1990 twenty Pintail were present, conspicuously in pairs, each brown female with a male, before their journey back to Iceland or Russia.

TUFTED DUCKS, POCHARDS and COOTS are diving birds and do not find deep enough water for large numbers. The resident MALLARDS of the Callows are swamped by an influx from Britain and the Continent in winter.

Changing clouds of LAPWINGS and GOLDEN PLOVERS, accompanied by the small

DUNLINS over the Callows are perhaps more memorable than the wildfowl because these waders, though equal in number to the wildfowl (about 30,000 of each on the Callows) mainly display themselves a few tight flocks, containing usually hundreds, often thousands, of birds. These can be encountered at any place along the Callows, even on the 'old Callows' south of Meelick where flat wet fields are ideal for their method of feeding. Most of the Lapwings in Ireland in winter are immigrants from England, Scotland and Continental Europe, and large flocks are scarce until October. No-one knows where Irish-bred Lapwings go for the winter. But we do know that most Lapwings return to the vicinity of their birth. So why should they leave the Callows ? Was a flock of 800 or so on the Little Brosna in August 1991 the population of Shannon breeders ?

Golden Plovers certainly do not breed on the Callows but in April birds in black-bellied breeding plumage are still seen and their courtship 'song' heard before they return to Iceland (Illus. 5.24) . Even more startling is the bright orange breeding plumage of the BLACK-TAILED GODWITS (Illus. 5.25) in March. A few, presumably members of these large winter flocks, stay and attempt to breed. This is a precarious situation, for the birds are wary and conspicuous breeders and normally rely on aggressive numbers for protection against Hooded Crows and other stealers of eggs. Their presence on the Callows in summer was worthy of note even a hundred years ago. Will the Callows still be host to the bird a hundred years from now ?

SNIPE on the Callows in winter are not often seen except when flushed from very wet fields which are often inaccessible. Snipe from Scotland and north-west Europe winter in Ireland, especially in years of harsh continental weather. In years when the floods are slow to recede, and breeding is delayed, a noticeable increase in Snipe breeding on the Callows is reported (13). Do a larger number of wintering birds choose to stay to breed on the Callows when conditions are ideal in April ? Curlews from Britain and the Continent also winter on the Callows and arrive as early as August.

REDSHANKS, the Icelandic and British/Irish/Continental races, winter in many thousands on estuaries in Ireland. The Callows are host to only a hundred or so. The piping of solitary birds can usually be heard among the wildfowl. The British/Irish race breeds on the Callows and increased Redshank activity and noise in early March (they feed in pairs at this time) are presumably these, even though breeding does not start in earnest until mid-April. An even scarcer, but equally regular, winter visitor to the Callows is the

Illus. 5.25 Black-tailed Godwit by Gordon D'Arcy 1992

Up to one tenth of the total Icelandic population of BLACK-TAILED GODWITS can be present on the Shannon Callows in winter and spring. The tight flocks are made spectacular as hundreds of birds turn their white wing bars and tails towards the observer. It is even more startling to encounter these birds in their bright orange breeding plumage in March before they fly back to their breeding grounds in Iceland.

GREENSHANK, longer legged than the Redshank and with a back of the subtlest grey in spring (in winter it presents a mottled and white appearance). Its three-noted call is often the first indication that a bird is within binocular range. The Greenshank is usually a solitary bird on the Callows but an unprecedented party of twenty-five were seen near Banagher in February 1992.

How can the Callows continue to be a prime destination for wintering birds ?

It is worth stating the obvious: wildfowl are a group of birds which are suited to feeding, breeding and roosting in environments in which water forms a major part; in which disturbance from Man is minimal; and safety from predators, especially at night, is maximal.

The shallow but extensive Shannon winter floods over the highly vegetated Callow fields are rarely, and in few places, more than one metre deep, and large areas often fluctuate on the borderline between flood and field. This provides the initial watery attraction for the seven main species of wildfowl which congregate here in great numbers. Each species has its own preferred method of feeding, created by their size, shape and form: Wigeon can walk on dry ground and graze grass; Teal, Mallards, Pintails and Swans can feed in progressively deeper water, without diving, owing to their size. Diving ducks such as Pochard and Tufted Duck, which must find food at depths of at least three metres, do not find the Callows attractive enough for large numbers, although a few will accurately seek out the drains and backwaters which must require underwater reconnaissance. Swans and Geese are strong enough to uproot certain plants and eat their hidden parts as well as grazing extensively. All species will take food, insect and plant debris, from the surface of the water, but Shovelers almost always do this with their wide and sieve-like bills.

The expansive flooded winter Callows can accommodate large numbers of wildfowl. A permanent restriction in the area flooded, or of the duration of flooded conditions, would reduce numbers by restricting accessible food and increasing disturbance. February and the first half of March is particularly important on the Callows for Wigeon and other birds.

Wildfowl are very wary and easily put off by human distrubance. The Callows are extensive enough to be relatively free from disturbance during the winter months, or to allow movement within the Callows as a response to temporary startling. Safe roosting sites are not always the same as the feeding sites. Geese once used the vast bogs for roosting and now often fly down to the waters of Lough Derg at dusk to roost in safety (in the company of Wigeon).

For the congregations of waders on the Callows lack of disturbance is again a prime factor along with the large areas of wet grassland on the borderline between flood and field, or just waterlogged by rain, where their food - soil invertebates - are impelled to be close to the surface.

Illus. 5.26 Whimbrels migrating by Gordon D'Arcy 1992

The universal phenomenon of bird migration is pariculary apparent on the Callows in the form of the unhurried day-time, low-level, northward flight of WHIMBRELS in late-April and early-May. Their seven note call is similar to one of cries of the Curlew, but the Whimbrel is a somewhat smaller bird and has a white and black stripe over the eye. It is locally called the 'Maybird'.

Peregrine Falcons

Peregrines do not breed in the low-lying Midlands. Even the Slieve Bloom mountains do not offer any cliff nesting sites. But in winter and autumn these falcons are reported hunting the Callows - one spent many hours of a September day at the eastern end of the Little Brosna. Peregrines have also been seen over Redwood Bog at the western end. Peregrines 'stoop' on their prey from a great height, killing it in mid-air. Prey items are super-abundant. The large flocks of ducks, gulls and waders, often on the wing over the Callows, are all potential food for the Peregrine. Peregrines were seen over the Callows on several occasions in the winter of 1991/2 - an unsuccessful stoop on a Lapwing, a rush of air followed by a headlong chase over the flood; in April 1992 (chasing Wigeon); and in autumn on the Little Brosna (picking a Black-tailed Godwit from among the thousands).

A quite different bird of prey, the HEN HARRIER, is a regular winter visitor along the whole stretch of Callows. Quite opposite in habit and form to the Peregrine, it makes low-level searches on long wings over the winter-brown vegetation and reedbeds, ignoring the flocks of waders to pounce on small mammals and birds. A Harrier plucked a Snipe from the summer hay at Banagher in 1992.

Passage migrants on the Callows

The Callows provide feeding sites during the movement of Icelandic WHIMBRELS (Illus. 5.26) along the far western edges of Europe, in late April and early May. Whimbrels use wet grasslands and estuaries on migration from their African wintering grounds to their breeding places in the far north. Many small parties of birds were in constant movement up the Shannon in 1987 (2) and Whimbrels were a notable sight up to ninety years ago (25). Two thousand or so Icelandic breeders pass through the Somerset Levels, in south-west England, in late-spring, taking mostly wireworms and caterpillars from the wet pasture (26). A north-westerly movement of Whimbrels over Cork harbour has been reported (27) and large numbers in some wet grasslands in Roscommon and Westmeath and also around the Loughs Corrib and Mask to the west. In 1954, one observer (25) reported the same number of birds in the same place on the Callows "day after day" and concluded (wrongly ?) that these were the same birds "hastening slowly to their breeding grounds". This is still the impression today as you watch these birds feeding and wheeling in late-April and May while other waders are breeding noisily about them. In late-April and early-May 1992 one observer estimated thousands of Whimbrels passing upriver (14).

RUFF, passing on migration from Africa to northern Europe, are seen singly or in very small parties in March and April but nothing is known of the importance of the Callows to the migration of this bird. In good spring light its orange legs and 'scaly', rather than 'mottled', plumage is striking. But the spectacular breeding plumage of white, chestnut, black, purple or buff neck feathers (its 'ruff') is rarely reported in Ireland and not yet on the Callows. However, in Britain it has been recolonising and spreading closer to Ireland since 1963 (18). The Callows are an ideal breeding habitat for the Ruff and if they (the Callows) can be kept in 'good condition' the Ruff may yet breed here.

What of southward 'autumn' passage on the Callows ? Very little is known to date. In 1992: Whimbrels in small numbers as early as 5 July; Golden Plovers as early as 12 July; Wheatears from 22 July (14) and with Pipits on 13 September.

Scarce birds on the Callows

The Shannon, with its great lakes, its ribbon of water and sense of space has always attracted birds which may seem out of place on inland habitats. CORMORANTS and COMMON TERNS nest on the Shannon lakes and follow the connecting River. Five SHELDUCKS passed upriver in May 1991. The recently confirmed observation of sixty or seventy LONG-TAILED SKUAS on the Shannon over Long Island, south of Athlone, one hundred and thirty years ago (1862) may occur again. A list of scarce birds on the Callows is given in Appendix 3. The long time span and few records reflects the lack of obsevers as well as a true scarcity of the species.

What birds pass unseen, or are seen but unrecorded, unconfirmed or unrecognised by the hundreds of people who spend all day on the river in hired boats, farmers walking their fields every morning, or birdwatchers expecting only the expected ?

In 1909 a Whimbrel-like GLOSSY IBIS (Illus. 5.27) was trapped near Banagher and still stands in a glass case in town. An equally exotic but luckier bird, a BLACK-WINGED STILT, one of an unprecedented twenty or more in Ireland in 1987, made its way up the Shannon in June, trailing long pink legs, and stayed a couple of days on the banks of Inchinalee Island. Seven CRANES walked by the River at Clonmacnoise in December 1957. A MARSH HARRIER hunted over the uncut hay meadows around Banagher in July 1991. A SANDWICH TERN passed up-river in April 1992 perhaps taking the best route between nesting colonies on the Shannon Estuary and Lower Lough Erne, after arriving from its tropical West African wintering grounds A GARGANEY duck (14) was briefly present a few days later.

Illus. 5.27 Glossy Ibis

The Glossy Ibis breeds in eastern Europe and Africa and visits Ireland very occasionally by accident. This bird was trapped on the Callows in Lusmagh in November 1909 by Dr. Dalton and stands perfectly preserved in Banagher. (Photo: S. Heery, courtesy of Mrs Liston, Banagher)

Illus. 6.1 Tractor cutting hay on the Callows in July, by Anne O'Connell 1992

A hay meadow is a tapestry of colour, sounds and smells made by a community of living plants, animals and birds, including the Corncrake. The term 'traditional' can most truly be given to the abundance of hay meadows, which are among the Callows most valuable assets. Their continued conservation value rests with a late cutting date and a sparing use of fertilizer. Abandonment to rank grass or reversion to summer grazing would certainly not be in the interests of conserving the unique 'community of living things'.

CHAPTER 6

"a struggle with the Shannon"

Farming on the Callows

No callow is the same

There is a difficulty in attempting to give a pen picture of farming and grassland management on the Callows. The Callows in general cannot be judged by one callow alone. The vagaries of pre-historic floodplain development have meant that each callow has its own characteristic grassland conditions. There has been no comprehensive survey of the soil or land conditions since 1837/8 when the callows in each of the one hundred and fifty townlands along the River were examined and described (1). Samuel Nicolson was employed by the Commissioners for the Improvement of the Navigation on the River Shannon to put a value on the Callows. He was also to predict the improvement in value should they be relieved of the floods as a consequence of the navigational improvements which were carried out in the following six years. (Incidently, the expected increase in value was said to be from £12,426. 6s. 6d. to £14,261. 17s. 5d.). His work was praised as having been "performed with great zeal and attention, as well as with great ability and judgement" and his team was probably the only people to walk the whole Callows until the Irish Wildbird Conservancy's survey of breeding birds in 1987. Indeed his descriptions provide a valuable insight into the landscape ecology of the today's Callows. The townland names are written prominently on the 6" scale Ordnance Survey maps. The physical nature of the land has probably not changed in one hundred and fifty years.

The following three examples illustrate the range of land conditions existing on the Callows, sometimes side by side.

Annagh, in the parish of Dorha, Co. Tipperary (at the head of the Little Brosna callows) - 285 acres.

"A most superior aluminous and calcareous loam, excellent meadow soil"

Charlestown, in the parish of Clonmacnoise, Co. Offaly - 67 acres.

"A portion of indifferent clayey and rocky meadow and pastureland, the rest peaty soil, of an indifferent quality, lies low."

Clonfert Seymour, in the parish of Clonfert, Co. Galway - 81 acres

"Inferior peaty-clay and peaty soils, graduating into boggy soils, part pasture, part meadow"

To outsiders travelling along the river in the nineteenth century the grasslands provided subjective images of great productivity even though its uncertainty due to floods was also acknowledged. Griffith's Valuation of 1854 put great store on the Callows and, in true estate agent's style, described the islands in the Shannon in the parish of Lusmagh as being of: "proverbial notoriety for abundant meadowcrops...anxiously sought after"

In 1801 the Callows were "richly clothed in meadow". In 1832 they provided "ample returns to their proprietors". In 1834 there were "luxuriant crops of herbage feeding innumerable herds". In 1838 there were "abundant crops of hay". In 1852 there were "rich meadowlands" and "cattle whose sleek sides and comfortable proportions tell of the richness of their pasture". In 1838 the Grand Canal Co. - "so intensively engaged in conveying cattle and sheep find it profitable to become farmers as well as carriers to provide food for animals under their charge" (2) - was leasing a forty acre island (was this 'Muckinish Cribbies' in Lusmagh ?) downstream of Banagher for £3.10s /acre. These impressions were not of course the full story. The land near the River was always the most productive. The other side of the coin was that farmers were "snatching a crop of inferior sedgy hay" (1873).

Ownership, past and present

The Callows grasslands are a very well-used agricultural resource even though the product may be seen as the result of a struggle with the Shannon. It may seem suprising that almost every square inch of Callows fields are used. Almost none lies idle at the present time.

The Shannon Callows are not a National Park, and only a two hundreth part is a Nature Reserve. Today, almost six hundred farmers work the Callows as part of their farms, so their holdings on these temperamental grasslands are necessarily small. Over half the individual holdings of hay meadow are less than four hectares and few are more than ten. Furthermore, these holdings are often fragmented so that one farmer may own two or three parcels of land on the same callow. This generally mirrors the upland farms to which the Callows belong. They are generally small and fragmented. Several farmers may share the grazing of a field.

At the beginning of the twentieth century large estates owned some correspondingly large tracts of Callowland, which were either rented to tenants or worked by the estate themselves. As these became vacant, for a variety of social and economic reasons, the Land Commission set about dividing the land between the tenants and farmers in that particular townland.

Around the 1830s, for the next hundred years, the Butson family of Clonfert owned about two thousand acres of upland, bog and callow, including Bishop's Islands. Christopher Butson was the last Bishop of Clonfert before the diocese was united with Killaloe and, though the Islands had been the property of the previous succession of Bishops, the lands passed to the Butson family. The Islands were then truly islands (three of them) separated by narrow stretches of water. Turn of the century maps show these narrow stretches to be marshland and today luxuriant wetland grasses, and a backwater locally called the Gabhlan (from 'forked stick'), rich in aquatic

life, occupy the space. This was probably the result of the lowering of the river-level after the mid-nineteenth century navigation improvements. Abundant hay was cropped from the "superior clayey loams for meadow and pasture" of the Islands, brought ashore by boat and stacked in large reeks on the roadside near the Grand Canal as witness to the fertility of this particular section of Callows. The Butson family left the area around 1934, but their callowland had been divided "long before that", possibly about 1908.

Drama accompanied the division of the callows in the townland of Clonburren. The Mathers family had owned Devenish Island and adjoining callows since the 1850s. For several years prior to 1916 local farmers rented and cropped hay from the fenceless callowland over which the ancient Pilgrim's Road ran. James Mathers, the landlord, finding himself with cattle and no-where to graze them, attempted to take over the callows for this purpose. The local opposition to this was great. In the words of a local ballad (3) " . . . with sticks and ashplants strong, Near five hundred marched along" and the cattle were driven off the land (twice). Amid rising tension the estate (including the callows) was sold to a committee of local farmers in 1916, then in 1920 divided among the tenants by the the Land Commission. The place was restored to the hay meadow it remains today. Even today, over much of Clonburren callows, almost every acre strip has a farmer (4).

The 'Banagher hay meadows' and adjoining "peaty and sandy pasture land" (on the north side of the esker along which the road to Banagher approaches the bridge, and from which the townland took its name) belonged to the estate of James Harter. He built the imposing Esker Schoolhouse and left his cryptic initials worked in the masonry over the doorway (Illus. 6.2). His callowland was divided as early as 1906, the pasture becoming shared by those who received strips of hay. The subsequent Land Commission map shows the unfenced strips of which the local tenants and farmers found themselves owners (Map 5).

This sort of division was echoed up and down the Callows. In the meantime, many of these strips have been amalgamated and swapped to form more practical units. The land depicted in Map 5 was consolidated into four fenced areas as late as 1990. But remnants of the strips still persist elsewhere on the Callows, barely wide enough to accommodate a modern rotary mower.

Intensification

When a farmer anywhere wishes to intensify his grassland management he considers any or all of the following options: he ploughs the land to plant high yielding grasses and clovers; he applies fertilizer, and sometimes herbicide, to bring those grasses to their full potential; he stocks the land with as many animals as is possible for as long as possible throughout the year; he cuts silage as many times as possible in the summer to guarantee fodder for the winter. Any hay he saves he cuts as early as possible in order to be able to graze his cattle on the new growth of grass. On wet land he digs and maintains drains to take both sub-surface water off the land and to drain away floods more quickly.

It is generally regarded that an increase in 'intensification' of grassland management leads to a decrease in the amount and variety of wildlife. It must also be said of the Callows that complete neglect will also lead to a decrease. Farming on the Callows has been variously described as 'unintensive', 'low input/low output', and even 'traditional'. Just how unintensive or traditional is it ?

Illus. 6.2 James Harter's cryptic initials above the door at Esker Schoolhouse.

Hay meadows north of the Martello tower opposite Banagher belonged to James Harter until divided in 1906. He built the imposing Esker Schoolhouse and left his cryptic initials in the masonry over the doorway. (photo: S. Heery)

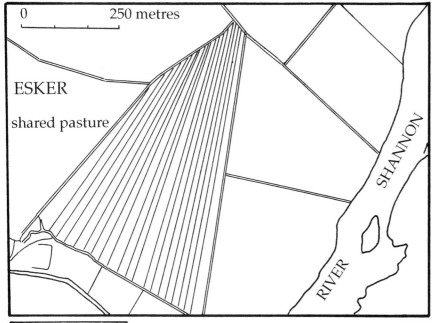

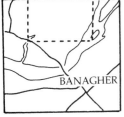

MAP 5   Land Commission divisions at Esker, Banagher.

Native species

Ploughed and reseeded land takes more than one full year to become established so this is not an option on the Callows, which are guaranteed to flood every year. The land would be vulnerable to the super-abundant seeds of Marsh Ragwort and Curled Dock (among others). Even over some of the embanked callows south of Meelick, which no longer floods, farmers are reluctant to plough and disturb the 'scraw' or ancient mat of roots which binds the surface of soft or peaty soil.

The pasture which is grazed, the hay which is saved and even the silage which is cut on the

Callows is composed of native grasses, sedges and herbs. There has never been any indication either from the farmers themselves or from the look of the land that any callow has ever been ploughed up and reseeded. There was a localised practice of spreading a 'hay mixture' over the field when the spring floods were receding and this may have introduced some grasses (Timothy, etc) but it is a long time since it was done (before 1920s) and the Callows plants will have long won the battle, if indeed they ever lost. Tiny areas of the highest Callowland close to tracks, well-drained and rarely flooded, may have been tilled for potatoes in the past. This happened at Lusmagh but again, this was so long ago that the flowers and grasses that inhabit these mounds today have all the great variety of a 'natural' grassland.

Do the Callows' farmers reap "a luxuriant growth of coarse grasses" from "sweet-scented meadows" or do they "snatch a crop of inferior sedgy hay" ? The answer is both, sometimes from the same long strip of land, because the Callows vegetation is patchy or very distinctly zoned. The quality and productivity of these native grasslands has not yet been quantified. At Clonmacnoise (5), not suprisingly, the productivity of the grassland (counted as the number of bales of hay produced per hectare) was lowest in the 'peatlands' and highest in the 'marshy grasslands'. The 'Upper Hay Meadows' or Star Sedge zone yielded 15 to 40 bales/ha depending on fertilizer input. The 'Lower Hay Meadows' or 'marshy grasslands' yielded 27 to 60 bales/ha. Reed Canary Grass (not present in the Clonmacnoise samples, but often a dominant grass of the Callows) and Reed Sweet Grass can yield much higher productivity than this. This has been shown in experiments in the U.K. and elsewhere.

Application of fertilisers and herbicides to these native grasslands

Since the 1960s farmers have been applying artificial fertilisers to their callows, but not as consistently or as regularly as they do to their upland fields. The reasons lie in the temperamental nature of the River, especially in April and May. Land may be too soft for machinery. Inorganic fertiliser is not a cheap commodity, many callows are far from the homestead and there is perceived risk that April/May floods will wash away their time and money. Compound fertilisers are mostly used (0.7.30; 10.10.20; 18.6.12), either in a planned way or to use up what is left over from other operations.

Three recent, but quite separate, questionaires to farmers suggest that one sixth of farmers rarely or never apply fertiliser to their callowland. Whatever their various reasons for this they should be encouraged to keep it that way as their fields will be found to be among the most botanically precious on the Callows. Although there are no figures available, I suspect that most fertiliser is put onto hay meadows and that much of the Callows pastureland remains unfertilised.

Many farmers do not necessarily see their species-rich grassland swards as a disadvantage. Indeed the 'sweetness' of the Callows hay, and the preference of stock to take it, is often commented upon. However, certain 'weed' species are thorns in the flesh of most. Meadowsweet (often called 'Agrimony' locally) in hay is perhaps the most hated, followed by Marsh Ragwort and Curled Dock. Early experiments with herbicides and Meadowsweet on the Callows took place on Bullock Island in the 1950s with the Department of Agriculture, the results of which are not to be found. Undoubtedly some farmers have recently used herbicide on their Callowland - in an attempt to counter Docks (Curled Dock 'twists' after application) and Plantains, to beat Marsh Ragwort that had sprung up and coloured a pasture yellow, or (in conjunction with fertiliser) in an attempt to create a grass-dominated sward. This increase in herbicide use, in widely separated parts of the Callows, seems to have come about since the middle 1980s, against a national trend away from such treatment. It might be assumed that many of the Callows holdings are not suitable for efficient herbicide treatment, being too varied in their proportions of grass, sedge and broad-leaved flowers. Nature conservation and herbicide on native grassland are certainly not compatible.

Stocking rates

The Callows pasture is mostly grazed by dry cattle from May until October but a few sheep and even fewer horses are regular inhabitants. Sheep have increased in recent years due to increased headage payments, despite the fact that sheep, wet land, liver fluke and foot rot thrive together. Sheep grazing Floating Sweetgrass in a flooded field in May (as at one location in 1992) is not recommended practice. The low-growing, ground-hugging sedge-rich pastures of the Callows peatlands seem made for sheep grazing.

Most of the Callows Lapwings and Redshanks nest in pasture and a high density of grazing animals in May and June means a high rate of destruction caused by the trampling of nests. A stocking rate of one animal (heifer) per hectare is a reasonable compromise between trampling risk and unwanted neglect, where waders can nest with a reasonable chance of success. Pasture use obviously varies throughout the Callows and has only been observed in passing. The peak number of grazing animals on the Callows in April, May and June 1987 (counted by observers who walked the whole length of the Callows three times) was 2,288 in May. This gave an average density (including the empty fields) of 1.2 animals per hectare of pasture. Occupied fields usually held between 1 and 2 animals per hectare. In one recent year eighty-five cattle occupied the thirty hectare Inishee Island where seventy pairs of wading birds were nesting. A very lively island, but nesting success must have been very shaky indeed !

Hay meadows on the Callows
- a unique resource

The epithet 'traditional' can be most truthfully applied to the abundance of hay meadows on the Callows. Since the onset of mechanisation in Irish farming in the mid-1960s (Illus.6.3) the amount of land given over to hay production has been steadily losing out to silage. In 1965 virtually all fodder production in Ireland was in the form of hay; by 1987 only half was saved as hay (6); but in 1991 over 95% of the Callows' fodder was still from hay meadows, not silage fields.

In 1987 almost one quarter of the Callows fields were set aside as hay meadows. Map 6 shows where they were. Annual counting of Corncrake since then (which has meant visiting

Illus. 6.3 Horse and hay-rake on the Callows at Cogran, Lusmagh in August 1966. Haymakers are: Teresa Sullivan, Nuala Sullivan and the late John Coughlan. (Photo: courtesy of Margaret Barton, Lusmagh).

all the meadows in search of the still common crex-crex sound of these birds) has confirmed the fact that most of these are 'permanent meadows' - hay has been saved from them year after year (barring the occasional summer flood) beyond the memories of the oldest people around the Callows. The map is, thus, little changed in 1992. These are not just odd fields of hay. They are blocks of virtually fenceless meadows up to one hundred hectares in area. In the middle of a late-June day they have an air of silence which is almost palpable, away from the intrusive sounds of balers, combines and silage chutes which are busy on the 'upland' grassland fields at this time.

Hay meadows on native grasslands are rare enough in Ireland, Britain and beyond - a collection of hay meadows as large of these is probably unique.

The past twenty-five years has seen a certain (unquantified) decline in the amount of hay meadows on the Callows. In less hurried days hay was made from the islands in the channel (Lehinch and Inishee, for example) and from fields in less accessible corners of the Callows, taken out by boat. Corncrakes must have abounded the Callows then. Samuel Nicolson's thorough description of the soil conditions on the Callows in 1837 indeed tells us that each of the islands of the Callows consist of variations on the theme of 'very rich dark clayey loam, suitable for meadow' (1).

A flower-rich meadow is a "tapestry of colours, smells and sounds made by a community of living plants and animals" and has been compared to a miniature tropical rain forest with its canopy of tall spreading flowers and grasses with a damp, humid under-storey of small herbs and seedlings, perfect, if temporary, micro-habitats for an abundance and variety of invertebrates on which breeding birds feed. But here the analogy ends. Each year the Rotary mower (and more rarely the slower, more 'traditional' Finger Bar mower) cuts swathes through this 'forest' and reaps a harvest of hay which is often praised for its 'sweetness' and attractiveness to cattle. The variety and abundance of plant species thrives on this annual cut (Illus. 6.1) .

But the timing of the cut is vital to both the farmer and the birds with nests or chicks in the meadow. Some of the the chicks of hay nesting birds are flying by late-June, but most do not fly until at least mid-July. The vulnerability of all hay-nesting birds (not only Corncrakes) was forcibly brought home at the end of July 1992 when a brood of well-grown Quail chicks was destroyed during mowing on the callows at Banagher; and also that summer two adult Water Rail were killed during mowing (Illus. 6.4).

Hay making on the Callows, as elsewhere, is at the mercy of the weather. A reasonable spell of fine weather needs to be forecast before the risk is taken. The Callows farmers have other considerations to colour their decision to start mowing. Slower growth on wetter (therefore colder) soils means that cutting dates may be four weeks later than on the warm soils of the 'upland'. Spring floods mean that the fertiliser boost to growth cannot start until mid-May. Often the few acres of hay on the Callows must wait for more pressing 'upland' tasks. And there is always, hanging over the operation, the spectre which is rare enough but none the less real (it happened in 1985), of summer floods. As a rule of thumb, these conditions have meant that, up to 1991, farmers hope to start their Callows hay making by the 1st July.

Three recent years illustrate the differences in timing. In 1991 most hay making did not start until mid-July, half was still not cut by mid-August, and some was cut and saved in September. In 1990 the entire mowing operation of the whole Callows was completed during the month of July. In 1992 hay making started in late-June. It came to a standstill in the wet weather of mid-July, to be resumed and completed in a feverish two fine weeks at the beginning of October. In the past eight years the Callows have had four wet summers and late cuts (1983, 1985, 1986, 1991), and four dry summers and early or normal cuts (1984, 1987, 1988, 1990).

Perhaps ten or fifteen per cent of the fodder from the Callows in 1991 was saved as 'bag' silage, and was cut in the middle of July. 'Bag' silage is ideally made from good quality, leafy grass slightly wilted (not dried), baled into big cylindrical bales, treated with additives and wrapped in black film plastic. The amount of this type of silage of course depends on the contractors available with the necessary machinery. In 1991 it was seen as a way to beat

Map 6   Hay meadows on the callows in 1987

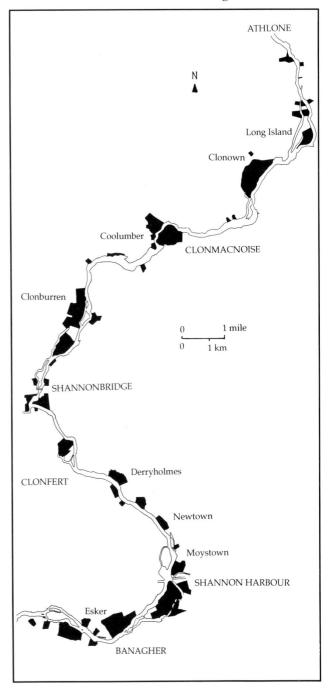

the wet weather which saw hay cut and left on the ground, turned and turned again in an attempt to dry it. But "you can't make a silk purse out of a sow's ear and in the same way, you can't make good quality silage with grass which was destined for haymaking but which was left on the ground for over a week in poor weather conditions" (7). In 1991 it was a case of poor silage is better than no hay. In a subsequent good year it will be interesting to see how many farmers opt for this expensive poor substitute for good hay.

The significance for bird conservation if big bale silage-making becomes acceptable is that the Callows will be cut consistently at the beginning of July which leaves no compensating late years for population recovery. The E.C. Environmentally Sensitive Areas grant scheme (Chapter 7) could take away the urgency to make hay in risky weather. Farmers who waited until August to cut hay in 1991 were not disappointed. But the grants would have to be high enough to compensate for losing the crop. In 1992 hay

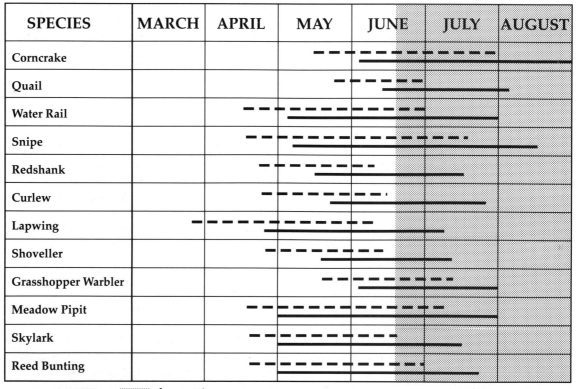

Illus. 6.4 Table 1., Birds which nest in the hay meadows of the Callows.

All these species are vulnerable at mowing time and 'Corncrake-friendly' mowing will help them all (courtesy of Ian Herbert).

SPECIES	MARCH	APRIL	MAY	JUNE	JULY	AUGUST
Corncrake						
Quail						
Water Rail						
Snipe						
Redshank						
Curlew						
Lapwing						
Shoveller						
Grasshopper Warbler						
Meadow Pipit						
Skylark						
Reed Bunting						

– – – – eggs
——— young
▒ haycutting season

making conditions were perfect up to the middle of July, but farmers who waited until after this were indeed very disappointed and had to wait until October to save their hay. Their only option was to graze the standing hay, or to cut and leave it (allowing next year's growth to be better).

In 1990 some farmers at Clonmacnoise made 'bag' silage in September from the aftergrass of an early July cut. The Callows are indeed not immune to change !

Aftergrazing

On the Derwent Ings, flood meadows in South Yorkshire, hay-making takes place in July and then the local farmers get together to decide on the date of 'Ings Breaking Day' - the day when cattle are allowed onto the Ings to graze. Cricklade Meadows on the Thames River in Wiltshire, which are famous for their rare Snake's-head Fritillary flowers, revert to communal grazing on 'Lammas Day' - 12 August - until 12 February (these are not flood meadows) when private owners once more take possession of their fenceless strips of hay meadow (8).

There is no such organised grazing of the grass growth after the hay cut on the Callows. Two extremes occur: no agreement has been reached (or attempted) and no stock ever tread and graze the meadows (for instance, on Clonmacnoise and over most of the Banagher meadows); or (as happens on Bullock Island) if grazing conditions are right after the last of the hay crop has been removed, cattle (and occasionally sheep) graze over the whole area. Sometimes none of the few fenced areas are

safe from animals seeking the young aftergrowth of grass from Reed Canary Grass to Timothy. In between these two extremes are individually-owned and fenced hay meadows where the aftergrass is used at the disgression of the owner. After October the risk of sudden rise of the River is too great and most cattle are evacuated.

It makes good economic sense to use the aftergrass and it can make good nature conservation sense also. Grazing suppresses the tall and quicker growing grasses and flowers and allows a greater variety of plants (such as the low-growing Cowslip, Adder's Tongue Fern and Eyebright) to survive, compete and appear again the following year. A grazed, low sward at the beginning of the next season is also attractive to Lapwings.

Drainage

Drainage ditches are the first signs of intensification of land-use on wet and flood-prone land, and the first attempts were made very early on. Bishop Bolton of Clonfert from 1722 to 1729 made "twelve miles of drains to the Shannon in four months work", and there is still a drain called Whitcombe's Drain named after a later Bishop Whitcombe of 1735. It appears that very many of the drains which cross today's Callows had been dug before 1837, if S. Nicolson's map is taken as the picture, and most before the turn of the nineteenth century. That is not to say that they were always functional. Nature continually works to choke drains with an array of aquatic vegetation and constant attention is needed. The fall in summer river-levels following the navigation works of 1840s probably renewed interest in keeping drains clear, but in 1882 G.H. Kinahan was complaining that many were neglected, and that waters from the bogs were poisoning the land.

Today the Callows are an expansive patchwork of often small, often fenceless parcels of native grassland farmed by people have an extra feel for a rare landscape which is at once agricultural and natural. The number of farmers who voluntarily attempted 'Corncrake friendly' methods of mowing in 1992 is witness to this 'feel for the callows'. Elsewhere in Ireland, Britain and beyond few farmers are constrained as much by distance, flooding, the weather and the growth of native grassland plants.

Illus. 6.5 Flooded Callows on the River Shannon near Banagher, Co. Offaly, April 1986 (Photo: Richard Nairn).

CHAPTER 7

The next 200 years?

Conservation on the Callows

Three strands

It is the purpose of nature conservation to retain as many wild species of plants and animals as possible in their natural habitats. The purpose of farming is to produce food and provide a living for the farming families. The purpose of tourism is to use an area's attractions to fill hotel and bed & breakfast accommodation. The continuation of the Callows as a 'special' place depends on bringing together these three different strands: the flora and fauna; the farming and local community; and the 'vagrant' tourist community.

Flora and fauna - Observation and Research on the Callows

In 1818 a 'Scientific Tourist in Ireland' (l) wrote one sentence on the botany of King's County (now Co. Offaly), describing it (with clear vision!) as being: "a virgin field but promising a great variety of aquatics"

In 1852 a pocket-sized book was produced - *'Three days on the Shannon'* (2) - which was ideal for travellers on the steam-boats of the day and almost as suitable for today's visitors. Despite the apparent brevity of his trip he recognised that "The naturalist, botanist, geologist find along its margins an equal field for the exercise of their respective studies but for the sportsman...affords sport such as is seldom seen in these islands"

Around 1863 (and probably later) the geologist G.H. Kinahan, in preparation for his book *'A Handy Book on the Reclamation of Wastelands'* (3), and an Annual Address to the Royal Geological Society in 1880, observed in detail the habits of geese on the Little Brosna, while contemplating ways to relieve the Callows of their yearly floods. "...the Geese come to their grassy feeding grounds (on the Little Brosna) about 10 a.m., and if not disturbed remain until 2 p.m. or 3 p.m., when they fly off to the bogs, to come back again at midnight, and remain on the callows a few hours." He also noted the presence of breeding Shovelers near Banagher at precisely the place where these birds (still rare breeders) nest today. His observations are quoted by Ussher and Warren (4).

In 1899 R.L. Praeger made his way on foot from Banagher by Shannon Harbour and noted Marsh Stitchwort, Fen Bedstraw, Trifid Bur-marigold and the Cyperus Sedge "in the swamps", and Purple Loosestrife, Yellow Loosestrife, Meadowsweet and Meadow Rue "in the rich flat meadows" (5).

In the twelve years 1892-1904 R.J. Ussher, in his own words, "began exploring Lough Derg and Lough Ree" and realised that the Shannon Valley had "aspects of bird-life almost absent from the Eastern and Southern parts of Ireland". This period culminated in a report of a trip by river from Banagher to Athlone in 1904 to describe birds met with (6). His account is brief and descriptive. Nevertheless, the Callows he describes could almost be today's, except that Dunlins were seen breeding in several places, Little Grebes were repeatedly met with and the Curlew was the most noticeable bird.

In 1934, despite the early promise of aquatic plants in 1818, and Praeger's first visit in 1899, he could still say in *The Botanist in Ireland*' (7) that "the broad Shannon, flowing along the western edge of the County, past Banagher, has been little explored in these parts". He noted the presence of Marsh Pea at Clonmacnoise, and Greater Water Parsnip, Fen Bedstraw, Marsh Stitchwort and, interestingly, the presence of Intermediate Bladderwort. The Bladderwort is usually associated with the acid, nutrient-poor peats of bogland. Is this rootless, floating, carnivorous aquatic plant still to be found in some quiet Callows ditches that flow from the bogs ?

But where in Ireland had been explored in this way up to this time ?

Botanical studies, even in the vast natural limestone rock garden of the Burren, Co Clare, which had been "famous far outside Ireland" for at least a century, had been conducted mostly in a "desultory way by dilettantes and tourists"

looking only for the Burren rarities (8). The agricultural landscape of the Callows probably had little attraction, a situation which indeed was not altered until the early 1970s.

In 1953 the Botanical Society of the British Isles (B.S.B.I.) initiated the Atlas of British Flora (9), recording the presence of plant species in ten-kilometre squares all around the country. Visits were probably made to the Callows at a number of points in the seven relevant squares as the B.S.B.I continue to do today. A visit to the embanked Callows at Meelick (in square M91) in 1991 discovered a new site for the Opposite-leaved Pondweed (*Groenlandia densa*) which is protected both in Ireland and Europe.

During the 1940s-1950s Major R.F. Ruttledge, born in 1899 (the year that R.L. Praeger first visited the Callows), who has been prolific in his contributions to Irish ornithology, had a special interest in wintering geese. During this period he made "many visits" to the Callows to estimate the population of White-fronted Geese at about one thousand (10). It was during this period that the existence of the Greenland race of White-fronts (with an orange-yellow bill) was first distinguished from the European race (with a pink bill) in Britain. Subsequent observations soon confirmed that the Callows geese (and all the Irish White-fronts) were from Greenland: "...they were of the Greenland race, as in all probability were a small flock on the River Shannon near Meelick, Co. Galway as early as 30 September" (1953) (11). The total world population of this quite separate race of goose was about twenty thousand at this time, three quarters of which wintered in Ireland (the rest in Scotland). The population today (in 1987) is about 23,000, half of which winters in Ireland.

In 1956, as part of a report on the flooding problem (12), a reference to the plant species of the Callows by the Department of Agriculture was as brief as Praeger's in 1899 but, of course, with a different emphasis - "In most cases the pasture species generally found are of an inferior type, the herbage being dominated by Meadowsweet, Horsetails, Hawksbeard and various other weeds, with some Timothy". This last grass was mentioned as a slight saving grace.

From the mid-1960s to mid-1970s interest in the international aspects of wintering wildfowl, through co-operation with the International Waterfowl Research Bureau, led the Irish Wildfowl Committee (later to become the Irish Wildbird Conservancy) to organise country-wide counts. Before the inclusion of the Callows in the first aerial survey (13) "...the birds of the River Shannon and its tributaries were little known" (14). A combination of the Irish Wildbird Conservancy's 'Wetlands Enquiry', aerial counts by the (then) Forest and Wildlife Service (F.W.S.), and regular monthly counts on the Little Brosna by FWS staff and local members of the National Association of Regional Game Councils (N.A.R.G.C) identified the Callows as holding numbers of wildfowl that were 'internationally important'. This period also led to the establishment of a Wildfowl Sanctuary on the Little Brosna. In addition, two Wildfowl Sanctuaries were established at this time on the narrow bog-enveloped River Suck Callows: one at Muckanagh (operated by the FWS) and one a little further south at Derrycahill (operated by voluntary agreement between local gun clubs).

In the early 1970s a brief list of plant species of the Little Brosna Callows was compiled as part of An Foras Forbartha's listing of Areas of Scientific Interest in Co. Tipperary, but the designation as such of the Callows was made on wildfowl criteria only (15). A review of A.S.I.s in Ireland and a change of name to Natural Heritage Areas is currently being undertaken by the National Parks and Wildlife Service.

In 1974 the first detailed look at the plant communites of the Callows was undertaken by FWS research staff. This was part of a general Irish wetland survey motivated partly by the need to survey wetland areas under an international treaty called the Ramsar Convention aimed at designating and protecting sites of importance to migrating wildfowl. This was the first detailed look, in Ireland, at the plant communities of wetlands which were not pure peatlands, and the data was included in a general review of Irish wetlands (16). The botanical landscape was described in detailed transects at six sites along the Callows and recorded 115 plant species (including the variety of aquatics promised one hundred and fifty six years ago years ago by the 'Scientific Tourist')

In 1980 The Forest and Wildlife Service initiated a ten year programme of conservation research on Greenland White-fronted geese, in response partly to a decline in numbers in the Midlands and the West of Ireland. Over the next ten years two separate groups of birds using the Callows were investigated in detail - a Lower Shannon group which used the Little Brosna callows, Shannon Harbour and the northern part of Lough Derg; and the mid-Shannon group which ranged from the River Suck to Clonmacnoise. Goose numbers for each range today are about the same at around 450.

In 1982, in response to (justified) fears about the destruction of wetland sites of both international and local importance, particularly through arterial drainage of the late 1970s, the National Association of Regional Game Councils (with help from its European umbrella organisation) commissioned the 'Irish Wetlands Survey' (17) . It catalogued a massive 700 wetland sites around the country, reiterated the international importance of the Callows and recommended the start of a long-term research programme in anticipation of any drainage proposals. This led to the first map of Callows plant communities, on the Little Brosna, funded by the N.A.R.G.C. and the British Ecological Society (18).

In 1984 the vegetation map of the Little Brosna was made use of in a study of the preferred diet of Greenland White-fronted Geese on the Callows (19) which meant many hours of cold and painstaking observation of the geese in the field, and of droppings in the laboratory for analysis of plant remains as clues to their diet.

During the period 1984-1987 the Irish Wildbird Conservancy and F.W.S. carried out a repeat of the earlier national wildfowl count. Recognising the special difficulties of counting birds on the wild and sinuous expanses of the Callows, four aerial counts were made in 1987 covering the whole area (including the Little Brosna and the main River). On a day in February 1987 a remarkable one fifth - twenty-one thousand - of all Ireland's Wigeon were resident on the Callows (20).

The callows enclosed by the bend in the River at Clonmacnoise are part of an area crowded with a unique collection of landscape features - eskers, pristine and harvested bogland, a marl lake fed by springs and a limestone pavement. Between 1984 and 1987 the Environmental Sciences Unit of Trinity College, Dublin conducted a very detailed study of the 'heritage' of the Clonmacnoise area which involved studying the social, natural, and historical aspects (21,22). The term 'Heritage Zone' was coined - an area where a coordinated effort might ensure that conservation and relative prosperity go hand in hand. Unfortunately, no official recognition of the concept has been forthcoming.

The map which this study produced of the plant communities on the Clonmacnoise callows was the second of its kind on the Callows, and depicted a mainly peaty area different in many ways from the mainly alluvial Little Brosna. In addition, the first detailed information on how the farmers see and manage their callows was collected. Farming practices are a vital aspect of the Callows and such information is invaluable and probably the most difficult to collect. A survey of breeding birds in the Heritage Zone coincided with the study mentioned below.

With an emphasis on the winter wildfowl and wader populations no mention had been made in any report of the birds (except Corncrake) which breed on the Callows. Inexplicably, only one record of a calling Corncrake in the vicinity of the Callows was sent to the organisers of the IWC Corncrake Survey of 1978 (23). Furthermore, this was recorded as being at "the Seven Churches, near Clonmacnoise" and consequently may have been from the ruins and not from the Callows.

In 1987, following a breeding wader survey of grazed, level sand dune grassland (called 'machair') area in North-west Ireland (24), and a promising pilot survey of three Callow areas in 1986 (25), the Irish Wildbird Conservancy undertook to census the Callows for breeding waders (26). With the invaluable aid of a cabin cruiser (sponsored by the owners Emerald Star Lines) seven observers walked every hectare and crossed every drain on the Callows from Athlone to Portumna (an obligatory three times for breeding wader surveys). The birds they encountered were suprisingly abundant and found to be one of the three largest concentrations of nesting wading birds in Ireland or Britain, and (because of the extensiveness of the Callows) the highest population for a single area. Corncrakes, casually counted in passing, calling in the early morning, gave a hint of the enormous significance of the Callows hay meadows for the bird.

More information on the vegetation was gathered during this survey, especially the locations of relatively 'undamaged' examples of the range of plant communities (27).

Since 1987 the numbers of breeding waders of one specific site on the Callows have been monitored and found to be stable over five years with the exception that breeding Snipe numbers are doubled during a year in which the floods are slow to fall in April (28) and that Lapwing nesting attempts are severely curtailed due to May flooding. The site is at Bullock Island (Shannon Harbour), which in 1991 became the location of the first Nature Reserve on the Callows, almost thirty hectares of old hay meadow, bought and managed by the Irish Wildbird Conservancy (and a some hectares bought by the Irish Wildlife Federation) for the benefit of nesting Corncrakes, waders and a large array of Callows bird and plant-life. In this area, at least, some hay is guaranteed to be still standing during August, a refuge for hay-nesting birds in the event of earlier and earlier hay cutting.

Ten years after the 1978 survey, which was itself a response to a perceived serious decline in numbers country-wide, the Irish Wildbird Conservancy conducted another country-wide Corncrake survey, knowing that they would record another decline (29). Corncrakes were systematically counted at night on the Callows and this time there was an enthusiastic response (from both observers and Corncrakes). One hundred and twenty-five males were found to be calling, occupying almost every hayfield on the Callows and probably no bird was missed. At this stage the Callows held one fifth of all the Irish Corncrakes.

In 1991 an analysis of the plant species composition of some of the grazed and mown Callows grasslands fields was published (30).

The Royal Society for the Protection of Birds (R.S.P.B.) had been researching the question of the Corncrakes' decline since 1985 when they carried out a very detailed study of the birds' requirements on the Western Isle of South Uist, in Scotland. The last two hundred or so Corncrakes in Britain were surviving in Scotland, but the density of calling birds was not as great as the Callows. In 1991 the R.S.P.B joined the I.W.C. in providing four 'Corncrake researchers' (two in Co. Fermanagh, one in Donegal and one on the Shannon Callows). For the first time the Callows Corncrakes were under scrutiny from the time they arrived from Africa in April to the time they left in September. Direct contact with the farmers from whose meadows the Corncrakes were

calling was the most important part of the this first year, and a special report on the year's work was written and distributed to them (31). By the time September came there was no-one in the locality who did not know the plight of the Corncrake, the importance of the Callows to them and the possible remedies. Volunteers helped to census the Callows again and the number was found to be one hundred and three, a drop of of 18% since 1988.

One of the reasons for conserving a semi-natural environment is that it can be used as an 'outdoor laboratory'. By this is meant collecting data from an area which is relatively undamaged by Man's activities in order to help solve environmental problems in another place or another time. From 1991 to 1993 the Callows are one of four sites (the others are in England, Spain and France) from which ecological scientists from six E.C. countries (Ireland, Netherlands, England, Spain, Germany and France) are gathering information from the callows at Clonmacnoise and the Little Brosna for just this purpose (32). These ecologists come from a wide range of disciplines: insects; larger invertebrates; soils; plant-life; the role of water above and below the ground; detailed observations and counts of the wintering congregations of birds, and of nesting wading birds.

In 1992 another Corncrake researcher roamed the Callows, and volunteers again counted the calling birds at night, in fear that they would hear nothing. In fact they heard ninety-five, a six percent decrease on 1991. In addition, one site on the Callows has been chosen for a last ditch attempt to study the detailed relation between mowing practices and Corncrake survival with methods used successfully six years earlier in Scotland. This involves attaching tiny harmless radio transmitters to the birds, especially the females, so that the exact movements of each individual bird can be tracked, especially at the critical time of mowing. The devices have a short life and fall off the bird long before they start their autumn migration.

The gathering and publishing of information and data on the ecological nature of the Callows is an essential tool to their conservation. What is there ? how can it change ? how is it changing ? are questions to be answered. But data alone does not ensure conservation. Up to 1987 the Somerset Levels have had forty-eight books and papers written about them, while their conservation value has declined. Agreed policies with other Callows interests, especially farming and navigation, are more important still.

The vibrant wildlife on wetlands in Ireland today (including the Callows) are but ghosts of those two hundred years ago. Will the wetlands two hundred years hence be but ghosts of today's or dare we hope they might even be better ?

Blackwater Bog

An opportunity exists to augment the wildlife of the Callows. In the first half of the twenty-first century thousands of hectares of 'new land' will be created in the vicinity of the Callows. Bord na Mona has been extracting peat from the surface of 10,000 ha of bogs which surround the Callows since the 1950s, and these will eventually reach the end of their working life (they will then be called 'cut-aways'). Many diverse uses are being considered, and an exciting opportunity exists to enhance the prosperity of the area. Bord na Mona has indicated that "20% (of the cut-aways) will be optimally used as wetlands, and Bord na Mona has begun to review how best to recreate habitats" (33).

Blackwater Bog Complex is considered by many to be particularly suited to wetland creation. Drainage will be difficult because the final level of the peat surface will be at, or below, the level of the summer Shannon, and permanent springs emerge from the eskers that surround it (springs have been responsible, so far, for the precarious survival of Fin Lough, a forty hectare lake-fen complex of "astonishingly diverse plant-life" at the northern extremities

of the Bog). Staff at the Blackwater Works are not waiting for the twenty-first century to recreate a wetland. In 1989 they dammed, instead of drained, another forty hectares, fed by a spring, at the southern end of the Bog and plan to enlarge it to 100 ha. Already Lapwings nest on the greening over peat and Black-headed Gulls and Moorhens nest among tall sedges which are springing up. Redshanks, Snipe, Pheasants, Mute Swans, and Coots may nest this year and even a Peregrine Falcon has found it profitable to harrass the Mallard and Wigeon which come and go in sometimes large numbers. Tourism is thriving here and the wetland can be viewed from the equally young 'Clonmacnoise and West Offaly Railway' (or Bog Train) which runs daily tours from the Blackwater Works.

Not far away, at Turraun in the Boora Bog cutaway, fifteen years of abandonment and the recent ceation of a hundred and twenty-five acre lake has attracted large numbers of wildfowl, including its first flock of Greenland White-fronted Geese ! (34)

The Callows in a Global context

The map showing the spring destinations and autumn arrivals of migratory birds to the Callows is one illustration of their place in an international context. The early 1980s was a time when Ireland joined many countries in promising and signing agreements to protect their particular combinations of wild species of flora and fauna. International wildlife law is as convoluted as other branches of law and is not going to be unravelled here. In any case, the aims of each agreement are interwoven with each other. Most importantly the emphasis is on protecting the *places* where the wild species live, and the Callows environment jumps out of the pages of each report, if only from between the lines.

In 1981 'The EEC Directive on the Conservation of Wildbirds' came into effect. Ireland has to ensure that no bird becomes extinct in its territory and this of course means protecting or recreating their habitats. This refers particulary to vulnerable, threatened and endangered species (called, in documentary jargon 'Annex 1 species') and migratory waterfowl. The herds of Whooper and Bewick's Swans, the clouds of Golden Plovers, the skeins of Greenland White-fronted Geese, the small migrating parties of Ruffs and the calling Corncrakes of the Callows belong to the Annex 1 list. The places where they dwell should be classified as Special Protection Areas (SPAs). An account of this EC 'Birds Directive' including very detailed and up-to-date information on the specific conservation requirements of listed birds has been published in Britain (35). To date, Ireland has classified twenty SPAs and the Callows, clearly qualifying, is listed by the Wildlife Service but not yet officially designated by the Government (36).

In 1982 'The Berne Convention', designed to protect flora and fauna, particularly those thought to be endangered, or likely to become endangered in the European region, came into effect in Ireland. There are no such plant species yet on the Callows (to join the Corncrake) but the Wildlife Act (1976) has led to the listing of such species in the Irish context in the form of the Flora Protection Order (1980), revised in 1987. The Opposite-leaved Pondweed is (*Groenlandia densa*) listed there.

In 1983 the 'Bonn Convention' came into effect. Ireland promised to take concerted action to ensure appropriate conservation and management of migratory species.

In 1984 'The Ramsar Convention' on wetlands came into effect (after a nine year delay). Ireland promised, amongst other things, to designate wetland areas which held over 20,000 migratory wetland birds (in 1987 the Callows held 60,000) or those with internationally important numbers of any single species (the Callows have seven). This considerably widens the species list of significance (see Chapter 5). Again, although clearly qualifying, the Callows

have not yet been designated a 'Ramsar wetland'. Ireland also promised to promote the 'wise use" of all wetlands.

The Shannon Callows have been included in the 'Manual of Most Important Bird Areas' in need of action financially supported by the European Community, (with particular regard to the survival of the Corncrake) but no action has been taken yet (36).

The Farming Community - 'Environmentally Sensitive Areas' (ESAs)

In modern Europe the future of wildlife depends upon agricultural policy. The wildlife on the Callows inhabits farmer's fields - fields which are part of the farmer's assets and income. It is often difficult for farmers and nature conservationists (apart from those who are both) to view the land in the same way. The nature conservationist must see the wider view - that semi-natural places are rare enough to be special and that the loss of even one field's diversity is part of the inexorable trend towards habitat loss. On the other hand, those living close to the banks of the expansive Callows by the pervading Shannon - farmers, local people and even nature conservationists - can be forgiven for sometimes assuming that there is no shortage of flooded grassland and hay meadow in Ireland or in Europe !

"The balance between the'environment' and the farmer's right to better himself has a particular poignancy in areas of the worst land. Here, very often, are the finest scenery and the most precious wildlife habitats - but here too are farmers starting from the lowest base of income." (37)

In 1985 the European Community officially recognised the fact that for most farmers in the Community wildlife on their farm was not, and could not be, a priority since this invariably involves a loss of income. They introduced the concept of "Environmentally Sensitive Areas (ESA) " into Europe. Member countries (including Ireland) can designate an area an 'ESA' and farmers within that area can voluntarily be included in the payment of annual grants so long as they follow certain simple and practical prescribed practices aimed at sustaining the wildlife (or general environment). The Irish Wildbird Conservancy (I.W.C.) have detailed how an ESA on the Callows would work.

"The objective of an Environmentally Sensitive Area designation on the Callows is to maximise the contribution of agriculture to the conservation of landscape, flora and fauna, through voluntary management agreements for which farmers receive income support"

ESAs are primarily an agricultural measure borne out of the need to cut down on the infamous agricultural surpluses. Because environmentally sensitive areas in the broad sense are often (but not always) marginal places of low incomes, it is a social measure also. Money spent on conservation will be a welcome boost agricultural incomes. The Shannon Callows are considered by many to be a classic candidate for such a scheme - an area specially rich in wildlife and specially difficult for farming. The farms of which the Callows holdings are part are generally small, and farm incomes generally low.

How would an ESA work on the Callows ? What would the farmers have to do in order to qualify for a grant ? What would be the 'prescription' ? Nothing can of course be decided until the Government decides to designate the Callows an ESA. Then a management plan would be worked out between the Department of Agriculture, the Wildlife Service, voluntary conservation bodies and the Farmers' organisations. It would centre on three things. Firstly, the keeping of hay meadows and a relatively late cutting date to ensure an uninterrupted breeding season for all the hay-nesting birds. Secondly, controls on the use of fertiliser and herbicides on the Callows to ensure that the great diversity of grasses, sedges and flowers on the Callows remain.

Thirdly, keeping the favourable winter and spring flooding patterns, to ensure that winter wildfowl have food and refuge just before their migration away from the Callows. Spring flooding ensures that characteristic wetland plants (many of which provide food for the wildfowl, and many of which are uncommon or rare elsewhere) continue to thrive over most of the Callows, and that wading birds find conditions ideal at the start of their nesting season.

The I.W.C. have detailed five long-term conservation aims to accompany the ESA 'prescription': to co-ordinate the activities of different bodies working on the Shannon; to develop a plan for research and monitoring; encourage the creation of nature reserves where wildlife can be enhanced; to increase the no-shooting areas on the Callows; and to ensure a sensitive tourist infra-structure in the area.

The Callows deserve to have a detailed and serious, long-term, imaginative and successful management plan.

The concept of Environmentally Sensitive Areas is new and original and still in its infancy. The successes and failures of schemes in Britain can be instructive. Two areas in Britain, comparable to the Callows but with much more immediate threats, such as ploughing, have had very different experiences in their ESA schemes. On the Norfolk Broads 'grazing marshes' in East Anglia the scheme is seen to be a success because it was built upon a previous well thought-out arrangement between landowners and local conservation bodies. On the Somerset Levels the scheme has failed to stem a catastrophic decline in breeding waders, mainly because control of water-levels was not in the prescription (38) (although the five-year review may improve the situation). The success of a scheme is seen to depend on exactly the right prescription being drawn up in very close consultation with the conservation bodies, the farmers and other relevant bodies such as those who control overall water-levels. This ensures that enough farmers think it worth their while to join the scheme (voluntarily) and what they are asked to do has the desired goal of maintaining wildlife diversity.

About one fifth of the Callows' farmers have not been in the habit of applying fertilizer to their callow fields for various reasons. (22,39,40) This is fortunate for the plant-life. As a postscript to this brief account of the ESA question the hope must be that in the final agreed prescription these farmers are not penalised for 'lack of management' in the past. Their fields are among the most precious on the Callows.

Shooting on the Callows

Wildfowling on the Shannon is the least documented of all areas in Ireland, even in the hey-day of such writing last century. A brief mention of shooting on the Callows belongs here because it is both landowners and visitors who take part in this activity on the Shannon. Local shooters, as elsewhere in the country, are generally associated with the local Gun Clubs which are affiliated to the National Association of Regional Game Councils (N.A.R.G.C.). However, not all would see themselves as wildfowlers, some preferring a drier land quarry species such as Pheasant. On the River and Callows it is Wigeon and Teal that are most commonly taken (being the most numerous), although Mallards are sought after for the table.

Unsupervised or badly supervised 'tourist' shooting is a well-documented problem during the shooting season, no less so on the Callows.

When dealing with wild migratory birds of international importance on a unique wetland, shooting must go hand-in-hand with conservation. One shot might bring down one bird but it interrupts the feeding of thousands. The national policy of the N.A.R.G.C. recognises this general rule, as does the end-date of the shooting season - January 31. Migratory birds, particularly geese, need time to feed undisturbed, to be in condition for the journey to the breeding grounds in March and April.

The creation of no-shooting wildfowl refuges are essential to the continuance of conservation, birdwatching, tourism and shooting on the Callows. Apart from the almost overwhelming difficulty of getting the voluntary agreement of the numerous landowners involved an any area, refuges must be chosen in places which have the remoteness, the right amount of flooding and the plant species to support very large numbers of birds. The negotiation and creation of the wildfowl refuge on the Little Brosna callows by the Wildlife Service in the mid-seventies was a vision waiting to happen. The 1990s cannot be imagined without such a refuge. The Callows may be extensive, but they are not extensive enough to accommodate disturbance by a high shooting pressure without corresponding refuges. The first decade of the 21st century cannot be imagined without at least one other large refuge on the Callows. The callows of the River Suck, north of Ballinasloe, has two within a few miles - one operated by the Wildlife Service at Muckanagh and one operated by voluntary agreement by the local gun clubs, just south of Ballyforan. The latter was an innovation which enhanced both conservation (a large goose flock inhabits both refuges) and local shooting.

The Visitors

If you hide a gem away in secret, and it is damaged, there is no-one to care. If it is on careful display, for all the world to see and admire, then the collective concern of all who have seen it, or read about it, affords it some protection.

Two types of visitors who interact with the Callows are perhaps illustrated by two entries in the 'remarks' section of the vistors' book in a local guest house in 1991, both international. A serious birder wrote - "Excellent Crex crex" and a visitor from USA wrote - "I love your Irish Corncrakes". It seems to be that this bird is the feature with which most 'non-specialist' visitors associate the Callows at the present time. This is understandable given the air of nostalgia which surrounds it, the relative ease of hearing its distinctive call, and excitement attached to the epithet 'endangered'. However, it would be foolish in the extreme to pin conservation hopes for the Callows on a species which may be uncontrollably facing extinction. Although the Callows may yet be the saviour of the Corncrake, the Corncrake should not be looked upon as the only saviour of the Callows. The immense variety and special nature of the Callows should be apparent in the pages of this book.

The Callows are part of the unique Midlands landscape, along with the bogs, eskers and the River itself, which is beginning to be marketed as an asset in the attraction of tourists to the area. The Offaly County Development Plan recognises that scenic views of special landscape features are essential and must be protected. They designate three views of the Callows and one of these, from a gateway in the hedge where the road touches the two hundred foot contour line, one and half miles out from Banagher towards Cloghan, must surely be the most spectacular of views in the Midlands. It would be an ideal location for a lay-by with an informative sign explaining the view.

There are a number of other places in the other Counties where the Callows can be viewed to effect (MAP 2) and from most of these the winter wildfowl and wading birds can be watched with whatever ease the weather allows. It is recommended that a day's birdwatching on the Callows should take in a number of these spots to make the most of light conditions, the movement of birds and the different characteristics of each callow. Flocks can be seen with the naked eye; species of birds can usually be distinguished through binoculars; while details of small, distant or otherwise elusive birds can be sorted out if a birdwatchers' telescope is handy. The Little Brosna callows continue to be a place where views of the large congregations of winter wildfowl can be guaranteed.

Views of the landscape and highly visible winter wildfowl from the public roads can be extolled without hesitation. One must be more circumspect in talking of other aspects of the Callows as far as visitors are concerned. The main breeding season for the Callows' wading birds is from the end of March to June and incessant disturbance at this time would deter their activity. It must be said that once the birds have begun to nest they are not very easily deterred. A Curlew was once discovered to be sitting on eggs ten metres away from an angler. Lapwings are especially vulnerable to disturbance. Their plaintive "pee-ee-wits", which pulls the heartstrings, are an indication that they have left their eggs, or have chicks hiding in the grass, at the mercy of Hooded Crows, so the observer should pass quickly on. The dawning hours before the world wakes is the best time to see and hear wading birds from vantage points at the Callows' edge, their dawn chorus can sometimes rival the woodland; a still dusk twilight is the best time to hear the rivetting and therapeutic 'drumming' of Snipe; night-time is the best time to hear the crexing Corncrakes in the vicinity of a hay meadow.

Directions on how to experience the plant-life must be even more circumspect as ninety-eight percent of the Callows fields are privately-owned and the plants are part of a grassland crop. Follow the Country Code; close all gates; respect private property; keep to tracks; and be extremely careful when examining aquatic plants in drainage ditches which can be treacherous.

It has been said that nature conservation is about "bringing as many wild species as possible into the next century". In seven years time that will mean the twenty-second century. I have tried to describe the special nature of the Callows, as it exists at the beginning of the 1990s. I have quoted a reference to the Callows in Chapter 4 from almost two hundred years ago. What of the next 200 years ? What of the next ten years ?

Illus. 8.1 Inishee Island, Esker by Lorraine Francis 1991

The ordinary-looking island of Inishee holds the highest densities of breeding wading birds on the Callows - in 1987 sixty pairs Redshank, Snipe, Lapwing and Curlew were attempting to breed on its thirty two hectares.

Epilogue

The last two decades of the twentieth century have seen more attention given to the temperamental fields alongside the River Shannon than ever before in their long history of ebbing and flowing floodwater. The Callows, and those who farm their grassland, have largely been ignored, surfacing briefly as an issue after bad floods which were forgotten during subsequent 'normal' years. There have been perhaps three other highlights in the Callows' history, periods when the word was on many other peoples' minds, not just those who were farming them: in the 1830s and 1840s, with surveys and works involved in navigational improvements; in the late 1920s, with the raising of an embankment, and the 'draining' of callows along the west side of the River south of Meelick during the Shannon Electrification Scheme; and in the 1950s and early 1960s, with the investigations of L.E. Rydell, a leading expert on flood control from the US Corps of Engineers. Recent attention is not a response to bad flooding, but part of a reluctant coming-of-age of environmental thinking which sees the Callows as a special place where there is still time for an comprehensive plan which takes in all interests, including nature.

This book is intended to be an introduction the Shannon Callows. It can only be an introduction, because it hardly breaks the surface of the highly complex (and largely unstudied) web of life that links the birds with the plants with the invertebrates with the soils, and the whole to flooding and water-levels, themselves a product of prehistoric landscapes and the weather. The web probably still has very many of its surpisingly robust strands still intact because technology has not yet found a way to simplify it; and the web is linked by the thread of migratory birds to other webs of life in the Arctic and the Tropics.

Numbers, names and lists are essential tools of the scientific view of nature. I consider myself lucky to have spent time on the Callows (often with numbers, names and lists in mind) in all seasons and at all times of the day and night, and have gained lasting impressions which have nothing to do with scientific investigation.

Inevitably, birds provide many of these impressions. The universal, and always wondrous, phemomenon of bird migration is particularly apparent on the Callows in the form of the unhurried, day-time, low-level, northward flight of Whimbrels in spring. The Sedge Warblers and Corncrakes arrive, as it were, overnight and it seems they never left. The immense variety of winter bird-life is reinforced by the sight of the Callows' smallest winter visitor, the Dunlin, feeding round the webbed feet of the Callows' largest, the Whooper Swan, and dwarfed by them. The spring and summer activity of birdlife centres around the necessity to raise at least one or two young successfully in the Callows' fields: a female Shoveler duck (a rare breeding bird in Ireland) leads her nine brown ducklings into the reeds (Illus. -) - an essential success because in a subsequent year all her eggs were lost; two very young, long-legged Redshank chicks wade amongst Floating Sweetgrass into a ditch of what seems to be precariously deep water, watched by noisy parents, anxious not because of the depth (waders can swim) but by the fact that I was watching them. And I have seen for myself the therapeutic effect of a twilight display of drumming Snipe.

A recent visitor, whose mind was weighted with troubles, was brought to a spot on the Callows a few days too early to hear the Corncrakes. Instead, in a still twilight too dark to see, he was treated to the sound of drumming Snipe, particularly loud in its crescendoes. The next morning he woke with the sound in his ears, the first time for ages that his troubles were not the first to greet him in the morning. Children, not biased by the concept of rarity, find the eerie bleating sound of Snipe after dark more exciting than the Corncrake's call.

A torchlight discovery of the Water Avens flower while counting Corncrake at Lusmagh; a small mound on the Little Brosna which, owing to a quirk of management, was crowded with Fragrant Orchids, other orchids and forty companion species; a rare Blue-eyed Grass found unexpectedly in a Rush-infested field near Portumna; neat heads of small, bold white flowers of Watercress (Illus. -) with very tall spikes of Heath Spotted Orchid in a field which, unusual for the Callows, could not decide whether it was a hay meadow or a marsh.

Birdwatcher's and botanists' stories can sometimes seem to rival anglers' tales and are fuelled by each visit.

The relative obscurity of the Callows in people's minds until recently is illustrated by an impression that this latest phase of attention has been one of suprises. When an film crew from Dublin brought their equipment over the callows to the Shannon's banks at Clonburren to film a documentary on local history in the early 1970s, a Corncrake dutifully suprised them closeby, resurrected, so it seemed, from extinction ! During the first (and, to date, only) all-Callows survey of breeding birds in 1987, observers stepped onto Inishee Island (Illus. 8.1) to an totally unsuspected cacophony of sound made by Lapwings, Redshanks, Snipe and Curlews which were nesting there in densities unsurpassed anywhere else on the Callows. A first encounter with the congregations of winter wildfowl on the Little Brosna is suprising enough but when researchers looked closely for the first time at the insects there, in the summer of 1991, they turned up a thoroughly unexpected Hoverfly species on the first day's sampling.

Almost any three hundred hectare stretch of the Callows would be the equivalent of a top grade Nature Reserve anywhere in Europe. But no such stretch can accommodate the variety and numbers of wild species which find refuge in the Callows as a whole - twelve times greater. The extent of the Callows is probably its single greatest asset - it allows many mutually exclusive features to co-exist. Winter wildfowl congregate in their thousands on the Little Brosna, but only two Corncrakes call; Lapwings can find no nest sites on the Banagher hay meadows, where ten Corncrakes call and many Snipe nest. The magenta Marsh Pea, the brilliant white Marsh Stitchwort, and the hazy cream Meadow Rue are soon ousted by grazing; Bog Pimpernel and Grass of Parnassus would not survive the shade of a hay meadow, and need peat in which to sink their roots; the yellow Creeping Jenny grows on wet alluvial pasture, the silvery False Oat Grass sends down a long tap root to reach water on high and dry alluvial meadow. Thirty Redshank pairs breeding on Inishee Island is fascinating enough - four hundred on the whole Callows is a good chunk of the Irish Redshank population.

The point that size is the Callows' greatest asset should not be laboured, but cannot be over-emphasied.

The Callows sometimes may seem 'wrongly' to be a disconnected series of wetlands because no road runs parallel to the River for long. Although the low hills of the esker ridges do their best to provide good vantage points, only short stretches can be seen at once. There is also a (wrong) perception that the place is so large and diverse, that flooding is so pervasive, that the wildlife can be left to get on with it alongside agricultural endeavours as it has for last few hundred years. This is only true up to a point. True in logistical terms - a single management body would find it difficult or impossible to attain the diversity achieved by over six hundred farmers managing their own callow, in their own time, over a thousand parcels of land.

But there is the well-known, but little heeded, phenomenon of creeping change in landscape and environmental matters, so that each generation of visitors is unaware of what went before. A farmer whose house abutts on the Callows is almost right in regarding the Corncrakes and the Geese to have 'gone'. He remembers the place being 'black with geese' and Corncrakes by his back door only twenty-five years ago. We who are new to the Callows get a kick out of forty Geese and a handful of Corncrakes. Technology in general, and agricultural technology in particular, will always eventually find a way of overcoming the difficulties to intensification, which is always to the detriment of wildlife. In the past thirty years, although there has been no decrease in the amount of flooding, the cutting date for the hay meadows has been brought inexorably forward from August to July and will regress further.

Attention on the three fronts - grants to farmers in recognition of the unique place they farm; environmental monitoring, research and wildlife conservation; boat- and land-based visitors of all shades - needs a locally-based, co-ordinated approach for the whole Callows. The presence of Irish Wildbird Conservancy Corncrake Fieldworkers on the Callows (as well as Royal Society for the Protection of Birds Corncrake Reseachers) for the past two summers has proved invaluable as far as public relations is concerned as well as providing on-the-spot observations of wildlife ranging far beyond the needs of the Corncrake. The activities and variety of the birdlife in summer, autumn, and spring was especially reinforced in detail by these full-time workers on the Callows in 1992.

The Callows need and deserve the permanent appointment of a team to liaise between farming, tourist and wildlife interests. The Department from which they come, the title they are given (warden, manager, advisor, fieldworker, ranger, co-ordinator - to throw in some possiblities) and their brief, may need careful consideration, but the continuance of the Callows as a special place where farming and wildlife co-exist should be the goal.

The concept of conservation occurs throughout this book, if sometimes only between the lines. A place where nature almost has the upper hand is so rare that it cannot be described nowadays without the conservation message. This message, especially on the agriculturally important Callows, does not mean letting nature take over. It means the wise use of money and manpower, certainly not an impossibly large amount of each.

Like the Burren and the Bogs, the Shannon Callows have a unique place in the wildlife landscape of Europe.

Appendix 1

Plant Species on the Callows

(species are all from land liable to floods)

GRASS FAMILY

Meadow Fescue	*Festuca pratensis*
Tall Fescue	*Festuca arundinacea*
Red Fescue	*Festuca rubra*
Perennial Rye-grass	*Lolium perenne*
Annual Meadow Grass	*Poa annua*
Rough Meadow Grass	*Poa trivialis*
Smooth Meadow Grass	*Poa pratensis*
Cock's Foot	*Dactylis glomerata*
Crested Dog's Tail	*Cynosurus cristatus*
Water Whorl Grass	*Catabrosa aquatica*
Quaking Grass	*Briza media*
Reed Sweet Grass	*Glyceria maxima*
Floating Sweet Grass	*Glyceria fluitans*
Plicate Sweet Grass	*Glyceria plicata*
Hybrid Sweet Grass	*G.x pedicellata*
Meadow Brome	*Bromus commutatus*
Couch Grass	*Elymus repens*
Downy Oat Grass	*Avenula pubescens*
False Oat Grass	*Arrhenatherum elatius*
Yellow Oat Grass	*Trisetum flavescens*
Tufted Hair Grass	*Deschampsia cespitosa*
Sweet Vernal Grass	*Anthoxanthum odoratum*
Yorkshire Fog	*Holcus lanatus*
Common Bent	*Agrostis capillaris*
Creeping Bent	*Agrostis stolonifera*
Timothy	*Phleum pratense*
Marsh Foxtail	*Alopecurus geniculatus*
Meadow Foxtail	*Alopecurus pratensis*
Reed Canary Grass	*Phalaris arundinacea*
Common Reed	*Phragmites australis*
Heath Grass	*Danthonia decumbens*
Purple Moor Grass	*Molinia caerulea*

SEDGE FAMILY

Bristle Club-rush	*Scirpus setaceus*
Common Club-rush	*Scirpus lacustris* subsp. *lacustris*
Cotton Grass	*Eriophorum angustifolium*
Few-flowered Spike-rush	*Eleocharis quinqueflora**
Common Spike-rush	*Eleocharis palustris*
Black Bog-rush	*Schoenus nigricans*
Greater Tussock-sedge	*Carex paniculata*
Lesser Tussock-sedge	*Carex diandra*
False Fox-sedge	*Carex otrubae*
Brown Sedge	*Carex disticha*
Oval sedge	*Carex ovalis*
Star Sedge	*Carex echinata*
Dioecious Sedge	*Carex dioica*
Hairy Sedge	*Carex hirta*
Slender Sedge	*Carex lasiocarpa*
Lesser Pond-sedge	*Carex acutiformis*
Cyperus Sedge	*Carex pseudocyperus**
Bottle Sedge	*Carex rostrata*
Bladder sedge	*Carex vesicaria*
Glaucous sedge	*Carex flacca*
Carnation Sedge	*Carex panicea*
Green-ribbed Sedge	*Carex binervis*
Tawny sedge	*Carex hostiana*
Yellow Sedge	*Carex flava* agg.
Common Yellow-sedge	*Carex demissa*
Long-stalked Yellow-sedge	*Carex lepidocarpa*
Spring-sedge	*Carex caryophyllea*
Tufted Sedge	*Carex elata*
Common Sedge	*Carex nigra*
Slender Tufted-sedge	*Carex acuta*
Flea Sedge	*Carex pulicaris*

RUSH FAMILY

Hard Rush	*Juncus inflexus*
Soft Rush	*Juncus effusus*
Compact Rush	*Juncus conglomeratus*
Toad Rush	*Juncus bufonius*
Blunt-flowered Rush	*Juncus subnodulosus**
Bulbous Rush	*Juncus bulbosus*
Jointed Rush	*Juncus articulatus*
Field Wood-rush	*Luzula campestris*

HORSETAIL FAMILY

Water Horsetail	*Equisetum fluviatile*
Marsh Horsetail	*Equisetum palustre*
Adder's tongue Fern	*Ophioglossum vulgatum**

WILLOW FAMILY

White Willow	*Salix alba*
Goat Willow	*Salix caprea*
Rusty Willow	*Salix cinerea* subsp. *oleifolia*
Crack Willow	*Salix fragilis*

Purple Willow	*Salix purpurea*
Osier	*Salix viminalis*
Almond-leaved Willow	*Salix trianda*

BIRCH FAMILY

Alder	*Alnus glutinosa*

DOCK FAMILY

Amphibious Bistort	*Polygonum amphibium*
Knotgrass	*Polygonum aviculare* agg.
Sorrel	*Rumex acetosa*
Curled Dock	*Rumex crispus*
Water Dock	*Rumex hydrolapathum*
Broad-leaved Dock	*Rumex obtusifolius*

PINK FAMILY

Marsh Stitchwort	*Stellaria palustris*
Lesser Stitchwort	*Stellaria graminea*
Common Mouse-ear	*Cerastium fontanum*
Pearlwort spp	*Sagina spp**
Ragged-Robin	*Lychnis flos-cuculi*

WATER-LILY FAMILY

White Water-lily	*Nymphaea alba*
Yellow Water-lily	*Nuphar lutea*

BUTTERCUP FAMILY

Marsh Marigold	*Caltha palustris*
Creeping Buttercup	*Ranunculus repens*
Meadow Buttercup	*Ranunculus acris*
Celery-leaved Buttercup	*Ranunculus sceleratus**
Lesser Spearwort	*Ranunculus flammula*
Greater Spearwort	*Ranunculus lingua*
Water Crowfoot	*Ranunculus aquatilis*
Meadow-rue	*Thalictrum flavum*

CABBAGE FAMILY

Great Yellow-cress	*Rorippa amphibia*
Creeping yellow-cress	*Rorippa sylvestris*
Marsh Yellow-cress	*Rorippa palustris*
Water-cress	*Nasturtium microphyllum*
Water-cress	*Nasturtium officinale*
Cuckoo-flower	*Cardamine pratensis*

GRASS OF PARNASSUS FAMILY

Grass of Parnassus	*Parnassia palustris**

ROSE FAMILY

Meadowsweet	*Filipendula ulmaria*

Marsh Cinquefoil	*Potentilla palustris*
Silverweed	*Potentilla anserina*
Tormentil	*Potentilla erecta*
Lady's Mantle	*Alchemilla filicaulis**
Water Avens	*Geum rivale**

PEA FAMILY

Tufted Vetch	*Vicia cracca*
Meadow Vetchling	*Lathyrus pratensis*
Marsh Pea	*Lathyrus palustris*
Black Medick	*Medicago lupulina**
Red Clover	*Trifolium pratense*
White Clover	*Trifolium repens*
Bird's Foot Trefoil	*Lotus corniculatus*

FLAX FAMILY

Fairy Flax	*Linum catharticum*

ST. JOHN'S-WORT FAMILY

Perforate St. John's-wort	*Hypericum perforatum*
Square-stalked St. John's-wort	*Hypericum tetrapterum*

LOOSESTRIFE FAMILY

Purple Loosestrife	*Lythrum salicaria*

WILLOWHERB FAMILY

Great Willowherb	*Epilobium hirsutum*
Marsh Willowherb	*Epilobium palustre*
Hoary Willowherb	*Epilobium parviflorum*

WATER MILFOIL FAMILY

Whorled Water Milfoil	*Myriophyllum verticillatum*
Spiked Water Milfoil	*Myriophyllum spicatum*

MARES-TAIL FAMILY

Mare's-tail	*Hippuris vulgaris*

CARROT FAMILY

Marsh Pennywort	*Hydrocotyle vulgaris*
Greater Water-parsnip	*Sium latifolium*
Lesser Water-parsnip	*Berula erecta*
Tubular Water-dropwort	*Oenanthe fistulosa*
River Water-dropwort	*Oenanthe fluviatilis*
Fine-leaved water-dropwort	*Oenanthe aquatica*
Fool's Water-cress	*Apium nodiflorum*
Wild Angelica	*Angelica sylvestris*

PRIMROSE FAMILY

Cowslip	*Primula veris*

Yellow Loosestrife	*Lysimachia vulgaris*
Creeping Jenny	*Lysimachia nummularia*
Bog Pimpernel	*Anagallis tenella*
Brookweed	*Samolus valerandi*

GENTIAN FAMILY

| Common Centaury | *Centaurium erythraea** |
| Yellow-wort | *Blackstonia perfoliata** |

BOGBEAN FAMILY

| Bogbean | *Menyanthes trifoliata* |

BEDSTRAW FAMILY

| Fen Bedstraw | *Galium uliginosum* |
| Marsh Bedstraw | *Galium palustre* |

BORAGE FAMILY

| Tufted Forget-me-not | *Myosotis laxa* |
| Water Forget-me-not | *Myosotis scorpioides* |

LABIATE FAMILY

Skull-cap	*Scutellaria galericulata**
Marsh Woundwort	*Stachys palustris*
Selfheal	*Prunella vulgaris*
Gypsywort	*Lycopus europaeus*
Water-mint	*Mentha aquatica*

NIGHTSHADE FAMILY

| Bittersweet | *Solanum dulcamara* |

FIGWORT FAMILY

Marsh Speedwell	*Veronica scutellata*
Brooklime	*Veronica beccabunga*
Blue Water-Speedwell	*Veronica anagallis-aquatica*
Pink Water-speedwell	*Veronica catenata*
Eyebright	*Euphrasia agg.**
Marsh Lousewort	*Pedicularis palustris*
Yellow-rattle	*Rhinanthus minor*

PLANTAIN FAMILY

Greater Plantain	*Plantago major*
Ribwort Plantain	*Plantago lanceolata*
Shoreweed	*Littorella uniflora*

VALERIAN FAMILY

| Common Valerian | *Valeriana officinalis* |

TEASEL FAMILY

| Devil's-bit Scabious | *Succisa pratensis* |

DAISY FAMILY

Hemp-agrimony	*Eupatorium cannabinum*
Daisy	*Bellis perennis*
Nodding Bur-marigold	*Bidens cernua*
Sneezewort	*Achillea ptarmica*
Oxe-eye Daisy	*Leucanthemum vulgare*
Marsh Ragwort	*Senecio aquaticus*
Creeping Thistle	*Cirsium arvense*
Meadow Thistle	*Cirsium dissectum*
Marsh Thistle	*Cirsium palustre*
Knapweed	*Centaurea nigra*
Rough Hawkbit	*Leontodon hispidus*
Autumn Hawkbit	*Leontodon autumnalis*
Dandelion	*Taraxacum* agg.
Rough Hawk's-beard	*Crepis biennis*
Beaked Hawk's-beard	*Crepis vesicaria*
Mouse-ear Hawks-weed	*Hieracium pilosella**

WATER-PLANTAIN FAMILY

Arrowhead	*Sagittaria sagittifolia*
Lesser Water-plantain	*Baldellia ranunculoides*
Water-plantain	*Alisma plantago-aquatica*

FLOWERING RUSH FAMILY

| Flowering Rush | *Butomus umbellatus** |

FROG-BIT FAMILY

| Frogbit | *Hydrocharis morsus-ranae* |
| Canadian Waterweed | *Elodea canadensis* |

ARROWGRASS FAMILY

| Marsh Arrowgrass | *Triglochin palustris* |

PONDWEED FAMILY

Broad-leaved Pondweed	*Potamogeton natans*
Lesser Pondweed	*Potamogeton pusillus*
Fen Pondweed	*Potamogeton coloratus*
Opposite-leaved Pondweed	*Groenlandia densa*

DAFFODIL FAMILY

| Summer Snowflake | *Leucojum aestivum** |

IRIS FAMILY

| Blue-eyed Grass | *Sisyrinchium bermudiana** |
| Yellow Iris/Flag | *Iris pseudacorus* |

DUCKWEED FAMILY

| Ivy-leaved Duckweed | *Lemna trisulca* |

Common Duckweed	*Lemna minor*
Fat Duckweed	*Lemna gibba**
Greater Duckweed	*Spirodela polyrhiza**

BUR-REED FAMILY

Branched Bur-reed	*Sparganium erectum*
Unbranched Bur-reed	*Sparganium emersum*
Least Bur-reed	*Sparganium minimum*

ORCHID FAMILY

Twayblade	*Listera ovata**
Lesser Butterfly Orchid	*Platanthera bifolia*
Fragrant Orchid	*Gymnadenia conopsea**
Early Marsh Orchid	*Dactylorhiza incarnata*
Common Spotted Orchid	*Dactylorhiza fuchsii*
Heath Spotted Orchid	*Dactylorhiza maculata*
Early Purple Orchid	*Orchis mascula**
Pyramidal Orchid	*Anacamptis pyramidalis*

BULRUSH FAMILY

Bulrush	*Typha latifolia*

All species seen since 1983. Authority (except those marked *): recent records of the Botanical Society of the British Isles (B.S.B.I.); and specimens collected by the author and identified at National Herbarium since 1983.

Appendix 2

Breeding, passage and winter birds on the Callows

Proved breeding on the Callows since 1987 (5,13):

Little Grebe,	*Tachybaptus ruficollis*
Great Crested Grebe,	*Podiceps cristatus*
Mute Swan,	*Cygnus olor*
Teal,	*Anas crecca*
Mallard,	*Anas platyrhynchos*
Shoveler,	*Anas clypeata*
Tufted Duck,	*Aythya fuligula*
Quail,	*Coturnix coturnix*
Water Rail,	*Rallus aquaticus*
Corncrake,	*Crex crex*
Moorhen,	*Gallinula chloropus*
Coot,	*Fulica atra*
Lapwing,	*Vanellus vanellus*
Snipe,	*Gallinago gallinago*
Black-tailed Godwit,	*Limosa limosa*
Curlew,	*Numenius arquata*
Redshank,	*Tringa totanus*

Common Sandpiper,	*Actitis hypoleucos*
Kingfisher,	*Alcedo atthis*
Skylark,	*Alauda arvensis*
Meadow Pipit	*Anthus pratensis*
Dunnock,	*Prunella modularis*
Whinchat,	*Saxicola rubetra*
Stonechat,	*Saxicola torquata*
Grasshopper Warbler,	*Locustella naevia*
Sedge Warbler,	*Acrocephalus schoenobaenus*
Willow Warbler,	*Phylloscopus trochilus*
Hooded Crow,	*Corvus corone*
Reed Bunting.	*Emberiza schoeniclus*

Passage birds:

Ruff,	*Philomachus pugnax*
Whimbrel	*Numenius phaeopus*

Winter birds regularly seen:

Little Grebe,	
Grey Heron,	*Ardea cinerea*
Cormorant	*Phalacrocorax carbo*
Mute Swan,	
Bewick's Swan	*Cygnus columbianus*
Whooper Swan,	*Cygnus cygnus*
Greenland White-fronted Goose,	*Anser albifrons flavirostris*
Wigeon,	*Anas penelope*
Teal,	
Mallard,	
Pintail,	*Anas acuta*
Gadwall	*Anas strepera*
Shoveler,	
Tufted Duck,	
Coot,	
Golden Plover,	*Pluvialis apricaria*
Lapwing,	
Dunlin,	*Calidris alpina*
Black-tailed Godwit,	
Snipe,	
Curlew,	
Redshank,	
Greenshank.	*Tringa nebularia*

Occasionally seen in winter:

Shelduck,	*Tadorna tadorna*
Pink-footed Goose,	*Anser brachyrhynchus*
Pochard,	*Aythya ferina*
Goldeneye,	*Bucephala clangula*
Red-breasted Merganser,	*Mergus serrator*
Knot,	*Calidris canutus*
Jack Snipe.	*Lymnocryptes minimus*

Appendix 3

Scarce birds to the Callows

from: Birds of the Brosnaland (6)

1893 Ferruginous Duck (*Aythya nyroca*) One shot, south of Athlone.

1909 Glossy Ibis (*Plegadis falcinellus*) One trapped near Banagher, November 14.

1940 Pink-footed Goose (*Anser brachyrhynchus*) One shot below Meelick.

1945 Pink-footed Goose (*Anser brachyrhynchus*) One shot at Banagher. (also in mid January 1946)

1946 Gadwall (*Anas strepera*) several shot between Banagher and Portumna.

1948 Garganey (*Anas querquedula*) One shot, Little Brosna, February 28.

from: Irish Bird Reports (24):

1957 Crane (*Grus grus*) Seven at Clonmacnoise, December 4

1960 Short-eared Owl (*Asio flammeus*) One, near Banagher, alongside the River Shannon, in Tipperary, September 1.

1960 Blue-winged Teal (*Anas discors*) One shot, near Banagher, September 1.

1973 Snow Goose, blue phase (*Anser caerulescens*) at Little Brosna, March 25.

1987 Gadwall (*Anas strepera*) One, male, on Shannon in Offaly, nr Long Island, 11 June. Twenty on Little Brosna, 28 November.

1987 Black-winged Stilt (*Himantopus himantopus*) One, Inchinalee Island, June.

1991 Marsh Harrier (*Circus aeruginosus*) One, Shannon Harbour, July.

from: Ist Mid-Shannon Bird Report (Irish Wildbird Conservancy)

1992 Pink-footed Goose (*Anser brachyrhynchus*) Six, Little Brosna, 5 November

1992 Ruff (*Philomachus pugnax*) Seven, Shannon Harbour, 12 March; Five, Clonmacnoise, end-November

1992 Dunlin (*Calidris alpina*) One, Bullock Island, 2 May

1992 Merlin (*Falco columbarius*) Adult male, Bullock Island, 2 August.

References

Chapter 1

1 Inglis, H.D. 1834 *Ireland in 1834*. Whittaker & Co., London.

2 Delany, R. 1987 *By Shannon's Shores*. Gill and Macmillan Ltd., Dublin.

3 Praeger, R.L. 1937 *The way that I went*. Figgis & Co. Ltd., Dublin. (1980 edition)

4 Mitchell, F. 1990 *The way that I followed*. Country House, Dublin.

5 Ruttledge, R.F., Ogilvie,M.A. 1979 The past and present status of the Greenland White-fronted Goose in Ireland and Britain. *Irish Birds* 1:3, 1-292

6 Steer,M. (ed) 1991 *Irish Rivers: Biology and Management*. Royal Irish Academy, Dublin.

7 Harvey,R. 1896 *The Shannon and its Lakes*. Hodges Figgis, Dublin.

8 Weld,I. 1832 *Statistical Survey of Co. Roscommon*. Royal Dublin Society.

9 Wakeman,W.F. 1852 *Three days on the Shannon*. Hodges and Smith, Dublin.

10 Lever,C. 1842 *Jack Hinton, the Guardsman* (1906 ed.). Macmillan & Co.

11 Ritchie,L. 1838 *Ireland Picturesque and Romantic*. Longmans, London.

12 Fallon,M. (ed) 1989 *Clonown: The history, traditions and culture of a South Roscommon community*. Clonown Community Centre.

13 Trodd,V. 1985 *Banagher on the Shannon*. (no publisher)

14 Grenham,J.J. 1983 *The customs and traditions of a rural community*. Moore Community Council

15 Kane,R. 1845 *The Industrial Resources of Ireland*. Hodges and Smith, Dublin

16 Fojt,W. 1992 *The Fens of the Biebrza Valley, Poland*. British Ecological Society Bulletin vol XXXIII: 3 208-211

17 Purseglove,J. 1988 *Taming the Flood*. Oxford University Press

18 Jeffrey,D.W., Moore,J.J., Newbould,P.J. 1984 Why Conserve Nature ? In: D.W. Jeffrey (ed) *Nature Conservation in Ireland: Progress and Problems*. Royal Irish Academy, Dublin

19 Curtis,T.G.F., McGough,H.N. 1988 *Irish Red Data Book Vol 1: Vascular Plants*. Stationery Office, Dublin.

20 Anon (eds) 1981 *The Lusmagh Herb: the annals of a country parish*. (no publisher)

21 Anon 1987 *Our Natural Heritage*. Union of Professional and Technical Civil Servants, Dublin.

22 Whilde,A. 1982 *Irish Wetlands Survey*. National Association of Regional Game Councils, Dublin.

Chapter 2

1 Nicolson,S. 1839 Valuation of callowlands between Lough Derg and Athlone. Appendix B in: *5th Report of the Commissioners for the Improvement of the Navigation of the River Shannon* H.M.S.O., Dublin

2 Coote,C.(Sir) 1801 *General view of agriculture and manufactures of the King's County with observations on means of improvement*. The Dublin Society

3 Mitchell,F. 1986 *Reading the Irish Landscape*. Country House, Dublin

4 Freeman,T.W. 1969 *Ireland*. Methuen & Co., London
5 Hooyer,A 1992 Unpublished data to EC STEP-FAEWA Project. (Office of Public Works, Dublin)
6 Stelfox,A.W., Kuiper,J.G., McMillan,N.F., Mitchell,G.F. 1972 The late-Glacial and Post-Glacial Mollusca of the White Bog, Co. Down. *Proceedings of the Royal Irish Academy* vol 72, Sect B: 185-205.
7 Ashworth,J.H. 1864 *The Saxon in Ireland*. (publisher not found)
8 Mitchell, G.F. 1990 *The way that I followed*. Country House, Dublin
9 Ellenberg,H. 1988 *Vegetation Ecology of Central Europe*. Cambridge University Press
10 Bellamy,D. 1985 *Bellamy's Ireland: The Wild Boglands*. Helm, London
11 other species: *Galium palustre, Mentha aquatica, Rubus fruticosus, Senecio aquaticus, Vicia cracca, Juncus effusus Myosotis scorpioides, Rumex acetosa, Caltha palustris, Lythrum salicaria, Lysimachia vulgaris, Scutellaria galericulata, Carex disticha, Ranunculus flammula, Iris pseudacorus, Nasturtium sp., Valeriana officinalis*.
12 A provisional account by A.Hooyer based on his own unpublished data.
13 boulder clay = a haphazard mixture of glacial debris of boulders to clay.
14 called 'permafrost' in the Arctic today.
15 de Buitlear,E. (ed) 1985 *Irish Rivers* Country House.

Chapter 3
1 Mitchell,G.F. 1990 *The way that I followed*. Country House, Dublin
2 Anon (An Irish Gentleman) 1818 The Scientific Tourist. J.Booth
3 Steer,M. (ed) 1991 *Irish Rivers: Biology and Management*. Royal Irish Academy, Dublin.
4 Hooyer,A. 1991 *Introduction to the Middle Shannon catchment*. Unpublished report to EC STEP FAEWA Project
5 Shaw,E 1991 *An Investigation of Major Shannon Floods*. Aer Lingus Young Scientists Project.
6 Weld,I. 1832 *Statistical Survey of County Roscommon*. Royal Dublin Society
7 Trench,H. 1879 *The Shannon floods. Lough Derg level*. (no publisher)
8 Fallon,M. (ed) 1989 *Clonown: the history, traditions and culture of a South Roscommon community*. Clonown Community Centre.
9 Herbert,I.J., Heery,S., Meredith,C.R.M. 1990 Distribution of breeding waders in relation to habitat features on the River Shannon callows at Shannon Harbour, Ireland, 1987-89. *Irish Birds* 4:2, 203-215
10 Coote,C.(Sir) 1801 *General view of agriculture and manufactures of the King's County with observations on means of improvement*. The Dublin Society
11 Nicolson,S. 1839 Valuation of callowlands between Lough Derg and Athlone. Appendix B in: *5th Report of the Commissioners for the Improvement of the Navigation of the River Shannon* H.M.S.O., Dublin
12 Tubridy,M. 1988 *Clonmacnoise Heritage Zone Project: a portfolio of management plans*. Final Report to the EEC Project no. 6611/85/08/1
13 Nairn,R.G.W. 1991 Floodplain agriculture in Ireland and its significance for bird conservation. In: Birds and Pastoralism. *Proceedings of the Second European Forum on Birds and Pastoralism, October 1990* Nature

Conservancy Council, Peterborough
14 EEC STEP-FAEWA "Functional Analysis of European Wetland Ecosystems"
15 Burgess,N.D., Evans,C.E., Thomas,G.J. 1990 Vegetation Change on the Ouse Washes Wetland, England, 1972-88 and Effects on their Conservation Importance. *Biological Conservation* 53 173-189
16 Whilde,A. 1982 *Irish Wetlands Survey*. National Association of Regional Game Councils, Dublin.
17 Lynn,M.A. 1977 The Shannon Drainage Problem. *Administration* 25:2
18 *Connaught Tribune*.
19 Kinahan,G.H. 1882 *A Handy book on the Reclamation of Wastelands, Ireland*. Hodges, Figgis & Co., Dublin
20 Rydell,L.E. 1956 *The River Shannon Flood Problem*. Stationery Office, Dublin
21 Delap, and Waller (Consultant Engineers) 1988 *Report on the Technical aspects of the River Shannon flooding*. Unpublished report to Irish Farmers' Association
22 *Connaught Tribune* 'Portumna Notes' 1927-29
23 Burrows,G. 1988 *Irish Times*.
24 Delany,R. 1987 *By Shannon's Shores*. Gill and Macmillan Ltd., Dublin.
25 Kane,R. 1845 *The Industrial Resources of Ireland*. Hodges and Smith, Dublin
26 Williams, C.W. 1936 *On Inland Navigation and the Application of Money Grants in aid of Public Works*. Vacher & Son, London.

Chapter 4
1 Tubridy,M. 1988 *Clonmacnoise Heritage Zone Project: a portfolio of management plans*. Final Report to the EEC Project no. 6611/85/08/1
2 Coote,C.(Sir) 1801 *General view of agriculture and manufactures of the King's County with observations on means of improvement*. The Dublin Society
3 Praeger,R.L. 1934 *The Botanist in Ireland*. Hodges Figgis & Co., Dublin
4 O'Connell,C (ed) 1987 *The I.P.C.C. Guide to Irish Peatlands*. Irish Peatlands Conservation Council. 'fen' = vegetation growing on black,calcium-rich, waterlogged peat
5 EC STEP on the Functional Analysis of European Wetland Ecosystems (no work yet published). see Office Office of Public Works.
6 Tansley,A.G. 1939 *The British Isles and their Vegetation*. Cambridge University Press
7 Heery,S. 1991 Plant communities of the grazed and mown grasslands of the River Shannon Callows. *Proceedings of the Royal Irish Academy*. 91, B, no. 1: 1-19
8 Haslam,S.M., Wolesley,P.A. 1981 *River Vegetation - its identification, assessment and management*. Cambridge University Press
9 Colenbrander,H.J. 1989 *Water in the Netherlands*. T.N.O Committee on Hydrological Research, The Hague.
10 Storer,B. 1987 *The Natural History of the Somerset Levels*. Dovecote Press, Wimbourne, Dorset
11 Hubbard,C.E. 1954 *Grasses*. Penguin Books
12 de Buitlear,E. (ed) 1985 *Irish Rivers*. Country House.

13 Praeger,R.L. 1899 *A Botanist in the Central Plain*. Irish Naturalist : 8
14 Robinson,L. 1991 *Save a Corncrake for Europe*. Sunday Independent 28th April

Chapter 5
1 Feehan,J.M. *The Magic of the Shannon*. Mercier Press, Dublin.
2 Nairn,R.G.W., Heery,S., Herbert,I.J. 1988 *The Shannon Callows 1987. Report of a survey of breeding birds and plant communities in the River Shannon floodplain*. Irish Wildbird Conservancy
3 Whilde,A. 1991 (draft) *Irish Vertebrate Red Data Book* Department of the Environment (Northern Ireland) in conjunction with National Parks and Wildlife Service (Republic of Ireland).
4 Ussher,R.J., Warren,R. 1900 *Birds of Ireland* Gurney and Jackson, London
5 Tubridy,M., Jeffrey, D.W. 1987 *The Heritage of Clonmacnoise* Co. Offaly Vocational Education Committee and Environmental Sciences Unit, Trinity College, Dublin
6 Trodd,V. (no date) *Birds of the Brosnaland* Co. Offaly Vocational Education Committee
7 O'Meara,M. 1979 Distribution and numbers of Corncrake in Ireland in 1978. *Irish Birds* 1:381-405
8 Mayes,E., Stowe,T.J. 1989 The status and distribution of Corncrake in Ireland, 1988. *Irish Birds* 4: 1-12
9 O'Gorman,F. (ed) (no date) *The Irish Wildlife Book*. John Coughlan
10 Stowe,T.J., Hudson,A.V. 1988 Corncrake studies in the Western Isles. Royal Society for the Protection of Birds *Conservation Review* 2: 38-42
11 McGuire,C. l991a *Corncrakes on the Shannon Callows* Unpublished report to Irish Wildbird Conservancy
12 Nairn,R.G.W., Herbert,I.J., Heery,S. 1988 Breeding waders and other wet grassland birds of the River Shannon Callows, Ireland. *Irish Birds* 3: 521-538
13 Herbert,I.J., Heery,S., Meredith,C.R.M. 1990 Distribution of breeding waders in relation to habitat features on the River Shannon callows at Shannonharbour, Ireland. *Irish Birds* 4:203-216
14 G. Tyler (personal communication)
15 Hutchinson,C.D. 1979 *Ireland's Wetlands and their Birds* Irish Wildbird Conservancy
16 Whilde,A. 1982 *Irish Wetlands Survey* National Association of Regional Game Councils, Dublin.
17 Sheppard,R. (in press) *Ireland's Wetland Wealth* Irish Wildbird Conservancy
18 Hutchinson,C.D. 1989 *Birds in Ireland* T & A.D. Poyser
19 Ruttledge,R.F., Ogilvie,M.A. 1979 The past and present status of the Greenland White-fronted Goose in Ireland and Britain. *Irish Birds* 1:3, 1-292.
20 Fallon,M. (ed) 1989 Clonown: *The history, traditions and culture of a South Roscommon community* Clonown Community Centre.
21 Mayes,E. 1984 *The diet of the Greenland White-fronted Goose in Ireland* Unpublished reoprt to Forest and Wildlife Service, Dublin
22 Mayes,E. 1991 The winter feeding ecology of Greenland White-fronted Geese (*Anser albifrons flavirostris*) on semi-natural grasslands and intensive farmland. *Ardea* 79: 295-304
23 Norriss,D.W., Wilson,J. 1988 Disturbance and flock size changes in Greenland White-fronted Geese wintering in Ireland. *Wildfowl* 39:63-70.
24 *Irish Bird Reports* Irish Wildbird Conservancy
25 Kennedy,P.G., Ruttledge,R.F., Scroope,C.F. 1954 *Birds of Ireland* Edinburgh
26 Ferns,P.N., Green,G.H., Round,P.D. 1979 Significance of the Somerset and Gwent Levels in Britain as feeding areas for migrant Whimbrels (Numenius phaeopus) *Biological Conservation* 16: 7-22
27 Pierce,S., Wilson,J. 1980 Spring migration of Whimbrels over Cork Harbour. *Irish Birds* 1:514-516
28 Ussher,R.J. 1904 Birds met with in the Shannon Valley. *Irish Naturalist* Vol XIII

Chapter 6
1 Nicolson,S. 1839 Valuation of callowlands between Lough Derg and Athlone. Appendix B in: *5th Report of the Commissioners for the Improvement of the Navigation of the River Shannon* H.M.S.O., Dublin
2 Bourke,S. 1838 Gleanings from the West of Ireland. *Morning Chronicle*
3 Grenham,J.J. 1983 *The customs and traditions of a rural community*. Moore Community Council
4 McGuire,C. l991a *Corncrakes on the Shannon Callows*. Unpublished report to the Irish Wildbird Conservancy.
5 Tubridy,M. 1988 *Clonmacnoise Heritage Zone: a portfolio of management plans*. Final Report to E.C. project no. 6611/85/08/1.
6 Nairn,R.,Murphy,W.E., O'Sullivan,A. 1991 *Corncrakes and Grassland Management: Ireland*. Report (draft) to Royal Society for the Protection of Birds
7 *Farmer's Journal* May 9, 1992.
8 Purseglove,J. 1988 *Taming the Flood*. Oxford University Press

Chapter 7
1 Anon (An Irish Gentleman) 1818 *The Scientific Tourist* J.Booth
2 Wakeman,W.F. 1852 *Three days on the Shannon* Hodges and Smith, Dublin.
3 Kinahan,G.H. 1882 *A Handy book on the Reclamation of Wastelands, Ireland* Hodges, Figgis & Co., Dublin
4 Ussher,R.J., Warren,R. 1900 *Birds of Ireland* Gurney and Jackson, London
5 Praeger,R.L. 1899 A Botanist in the Central Plain. *Irish Naturalist* : 8
6 Ussher,R.J. 1904 Birds met with in the Shannon Valley. *Irish Naturalist* Vol XIII
7 Praeger,R.L. 1934 *The Botanist in Ireland* Hodges Figgis & Co., Dublin
8 Nelson,C., Walsh,W. 1991 *The Burren*. Boethius Press, Kilkenny and The Conservancy of the Burren.
9 Perring,F.H., Walters,S.M. 1962 *Atlas of British Flora*. Botanical Society of the British Isles, London
10 Ruttledge,R.F., Hall-Watt,M. 1958 The distribution of status of wild geese in Ireland. *Bird Study* 5
11 *Irish Bird Report* 1953 Irish Wildbird Conservancy.

12 Rydell,L.E. 1956 *The River Shannon Flood Problem*. Stationery Office, Dublin

13 Cabot,D. 1967 Results of an aerial survey of Irish wildfowl and their wetlands. *Irish Wildbird Conservancy Publication no. 8.*

14 Hutchinson,C. 1979 *Ireland's wetlands and their birds*. Irish Wildbird Conservancy.

15 An Foras Forbartha 1981 *Areas of Scientific Interest in Ireland*. An Foras Forbartha, Dublin

16 O'Connell,M., Ryan,J., MacGowran,B.A. 1984 Wetland communities in Ireland: a phytosociological review. In: P.D.Moore (ed) *European Mires* Academic Press.

17 Whilde,A. 1982 *Irish Wetlands Survey* National Association of Regional Game Councils, Dublin.

18 Heery,S. 1983 *A Vegetation Study of the Little Brosna Floodplain Grasslands.* Unpublished report to National Association of Regional Game Councils

19 Mayes,E. 1991 The winter feeding ecology of Greenland White-fronted Geese (*Anser albifrons flavirostris*) on semi-natural grasslands and intensive farmland. *Ardea* 79: 295-304

20 Sheppard,R. (in press) *Ireland's Wetland Wealth*. Irish Wildbird Conservancy

21 Tubridy,M., Jeffrey,D.W. (eds) 1987 *The Heritage of Clonmacnoise*. Co. Offaly Vocational Education Committee and Environmental Sciences Unit, Trinity College, Dublin

22 Tubridy,M. 1988 *Clonmacnoise Heritage Zone: a portfolio of management plans*. Final Report to E.C. project no. 6611/85/08/1.

23 O'Meara,M. 1979 Distribution and numbers of Corncrake in Ireland in 1978. *Irish Birds* 1:381-405

24 Nairn,R.G.W., Sheppard,J.R. 1987 Breeding waders of sand-dune machair in north-west Ireland. *Irish Birds* 3: 53-70

25 Nairn,R.G.W., Herbert,I.J. 1986 *Breeding waders in the River Shannon Callows. A sample survey*. Unpublished report to Irish Wildbird Conservancy.

26 Nairn,R.G.W., Herbert,I.J., Heery,S. 1988 Breeding waders and other wet grassland birds of the River Shannon Callows, Ireland. *Irish Birds* 3: 521-538

27 Nairn,R.G.W., Heery,S., Herbert, I.J. 1988 *Shannon Callows 1987 - report of a survey of breeding birds and plant communities in the River Shannon floodplain Ireland*. Unpublished report for Irish Wildbird Consevancy.

28 Herbert,I.J., Heery,S., Meredith,C.R.M. 1990 Distribution of breeding waders in relation to habitat features on the River Shannon callows at Shannonharbour, Ireland. *Irish Birds* 4:203-216

29 Mayes,E., Stowe,T.J. 1989 The status and distribution of Corncrake in Ireland, 1988. *Irish Birds* 4: 1-12

30 Heery,S. 1991 The Plant communities of grazed and mown grasslands of the River Shannon Callows. *Proceedings of the Royal Irish Academy*. 91 B, no 1: 1-19

31 McGuire,C. l991b *Corncrakes on the Shannon Callows - report to the farmers of the Callows*. Irish Wildbird Conservancy

32 EC STEP Project. Functional Analysis of European Wetland Ecosystems

33 Anon 1990 *Conservation and Corporate Responsibilty*. Bord na Mona

34 Kavanagh,B. 1992 What future cutaway bogs ? *Living Heritage* vol 9 no 1

35 Stroud,D.A., Mudge,G.P., Pienkowski,M.W. 1991 *Protecting Internationally Important Bird Sites*. Joint Nature Conservation Committee, Peterborough.

36 Mayes,E. 1991 *Protecting Ireland's Important Bird Sites*. Unpublished report to Irish Wildbird Conservancy.

37 Viney,M. 1990 Minding the meadows *Irish Times*, March 3

38 Warland,M., Woods,A. 1989 Articles in: *Naturopa* no 63 (Council for Europe)

39 McGuire,C. l991a *Corncrakes on the Shannon Callows*. Unpublished report to Irish Wildbird Conservancy

40 Smith,M., Madden,J., Malone,F. 1988 *The Shannon Callows at Esker, Cushcallow, Reask and Shannon Harbour*. Banagher Vocational (Aer Lingus Young Scientist Project)

Related reading

Further reading on the subject of the River Shannon, the recent and more distant past history of the land through which it flows can be found in the following books, with their own bibliographies:

By Shannon's Shores, by Ruth Delany 1987 Gill & MacMillan.
Shell Guide to the Shannon, edited by Ruth Delany 1989 Gill & MacMillan.
The Magic of the Shannon, by John M. Feehan 1980 Mercier Press.
Shannon Through her Literature, by Padraic O'Farrell 1983 Mercier Press.
Looking Around: Aspects of the Local Environment, by James Scully 1985 Birr - Banagher I.N.T.O. A very well-illustrated book on the natural and historical environment of the area around the mid-Shannon, aimed at Primary School children.
The Heritage of Clonmacnoise, by Mary Tubridy and D.W.Jeffrey 1987 Environmental Sciences Unit, Trinity College with County Offaly Vocational Educational Committee.

It is impossible to provide details of identification of the birds and plants mentioned in a book such as this. It may be useful, therefore, to have one of the many available good illustrated field guides on bird and plants (including sedges and grasses) to hand.

For birds in an Irish context:

The Guide to the Birds of Ireland, by Gordon D'Arcy 1981 Dublin. A short illustrated guide to identification.
The Birds of Ireland, by Gordon D'Arcy 1986 Belfast. A longer, more informative illustrated book.
Birds in Ireland, by Clive Hutchinson 1989 T & D Poyser, Calton. A very detailed review of birds and birdwatching in Ireland.
Ireland's Wetlands and their Birds, by Clive Hutchinson, Irish Wildbird Conservancy, Dublin.
Irish Vertebrate Red Data Book, by Anthony Whilde (in press) D.o.I (N.I.) in conjunction with National Parks and Wildlife Service (Republic of Ireland). Details of rare and endangered vertebrates, including birds, in Ireland.

Birds of the Brosnaland, by Valentine Trodd, Co. Offaly Vocational Eductational Committee. A book about the winter birds and birdwatching on the Little Brosna.

For plants in an Irish context:

An Irish Flora, by D.A.Webb 1977 Dundalgan Press. Not illustrated, but contains essential details of identification and distribution of all Irish plant species.

Census catalogue of the Flora of Ireland, by Mary J.P.Scannell and Donal M. Synnott 1987 Stationery Office Dublin. Not illustrated, but contains details of distribution of Irish plant species in forty regions (called 'vice-counties'), including names in English, Irish and Latin.

Irish Red Data Book: Vascular Plants, by T.G.F. Curtis and H.N.McGough 1988 Stationery Office, Dublin. Detailed accounts of very rare and endangered plants in Ireland.

Index

Plain numbers refer to text entries, **bold** numbers to illustrations.

BIRDS (Common names)

BIRDS (Scientific names)

PLANTS (Common Names)

PLANTS (Scientific names)

GENERAL and PLACE-NAMES

Other Tír Eolas Publications

Kinvara,
A Ramblers Guide & Map   £1.95

Kiltartan Country,
A Ramblers Guide & Map   £1.95

The Burren Series:
Ballyvaughan,
A Ramblers Guide & Map   £1.95

Kilfenora,
A Ramblers Guide & Map   £1.95

O'Brien Country,
A Ramblers Guide & Map   £1.95

Medieval Galway,
A Ramblers Guide & Map   £3.50

"A Quiet Pint In Kinvara"
A Poem by Richard Tillingast
with Drawings by Anne Korff
Published by Tír Eolas & Salmon Publishing
ISBN 0 948339 632   £3.95

The Book of the Burren
ISBN 1 873821 00X   P.B. £ 9.95
ISBN 1 873821 050   H.B. £15.95

Not a Word of a Lie
by Bridie Quinn-Conroy
ISBN 1 873821 018   P.B. £ 6.95